The Cost of
Citizenship

The Cost of

Citizenship

A Family's Battle Against Persecution and Sacrifices for Freedom

Andres Gamboa-Barrera

Based on a true story.

ISBN: 978-1-7368047-0-4 (e-book)
ISBN: 978-1-7368047-1-1 (paperback)
ISBN: 978-1-7368047-2-8 (hardcover)

CONTENTS

INTRODUCTION

Wow. What a journey.

In a way, I guess you can say I have been working on this since the very first day I moved here, or maybe it came about as a result of the different posts I have shared on social media. As always, I would like to start with the "why" behind this book.

There were so many projects, goals, and tasks that I had on my plate. However, when it came to sharing the story of my family, this had always been a project I knew I would have to complete before too long. I decided to pursue sharing this story in detail mainly because I wanted to honor my parents. Ultimately, that is who this specific story is about. I wanted to ensure that all they went through, sacrificed, and achieved is remembered for generations to come. At the very least, they deserve that.

Secondly, this story in general is actually about all immigrants, documented or otherwise, who come to the United States in order to survive. This book is not meant to persuade, or to serve as an argument politically. However, as I intend to leave future generations with some perspective, I intend to leave any reader with the same perspective. If you are reading this in the United States, then it is likely that either you, or at most, your great-grandparents share this story. Mama, Papa, Danny, and Juli, I hope you some of these words help give you an idea of how much you all mean to me.

I would like to take this time to also thank several people:

My parents, my siblings, and the rest of our family, my grandma Feliza for her support, encouragement, and belief. Also to Dr. Stephen Joel for his kind words, my editor Sandi, Jared, Amy, Ben, and everyone at Self-Publishing School for all of their work in making this whole thing possible in less than two months. There are several others who deserve praise; these are all of the people who helped us along the way. While my parents worked extremely hard for their accomplishments, there can be no question that without the kindness of several people, we would have been in peril. These include educators, friends, and strangers.

Last thing before you begin: Please understand that so far this has been the most difficult task I have completed in my life, I aim to conquer bigger fears in the future. Reliving some of these memories, overcoming the fears of the past, the insecurities of sharing these details, and wrestling with the losses sustained over the years, all at the same time, changed my life. This right here is me communicating that this is something I care about, deeply. I hope it is worth it to you.

If we have met and you are here, thank you. I am a better person for having known you. I hope to return the favor with this.

Enjoy,

Andrés

FOREWORD FROM DR. STEVE JOEL

In December 2006, the community of Grand Island, Nebraska, experienced an immigration raid by federal authorities. This event devastated the community as many hard-working people at the local manufacturing plant were detained. In my role as superintendent of the local school system, I knew this event would impact the lives of many children who had hugged their parents goodbye that morning.

I first met Andrés Gamboa-Barrera in 2008 while visiting one of Grand Island's middle schools. I remember him asking me, the superintendent of schools, several questions related to our curriculum and the opportunities available for students. I further recall him being bold enough to offer suggestions for me to consider as our district and community sought ways to become more welcoming to immigrant children and their families. The young man left an indelible impression upon me that sparked my curiosity to learn more about Andrés.

While serving as chair of the Multi-Cultural Coalition, I was able to get to know both of Andrés' parents. They were hard workers, very unassuming but always happy. While they never shared their story, I always felt they were grateful to be in Grand Island and the United States. I know their son definitely felt that way and it showed in all of my interactions with him.

As the district and community continued to heal from the horrific immigration raid, I was searching for strategies to help our teachers and administrators learn more about the children we were serving. When I asked Andrés to speak at our opening convocation, little did I (nor anyone in the auditorium that day) know how impactful Andrés' story would be. You see, as educators, we often assume that children come ready to learn and that they should be able to forget their past and focus on their future. But, that day, an entire K-12 faculty understood, in vivid detail, what one family encountered while fleeing terrorists and coming to a country where they knew very little of the language and culture.

The Cost of Citizenship is a story about courage, resilience, dedication and commitment that a family undertook to seek out a safer and more productive life. The challenges experienced by Andrés offer motivation for others that are trying to learn how to navigate life in a new, unfamiliar culture.

I am incredibly proud of Andrés for sharing his story so that his experience can lift up others who are trying to navigate a strange new world. His desire to give back is what drives him as a successful adult that worked hard, loved his family and treated everyone with dignity and respect.

I am pleased he has decided to tell his story to the United States. It is certainly worth hearing.

Dr. Steve Joel, Superintendent
Lincoln Public Schools
Lincoln, Nebraska

SOME WORDS FROM MY FAMILY

Daniel Leonardo Gamboa Barrera

Perhaps the greatest blessing given to us is having a family to share our life with, to be with us during our significant triumphs and to support us during our most trying times. The stories shared in this book will always have a special place in my heart. These are the moments that shaped my family. I feel an exceptional privilege to be able to share these moments in my life with my brother Andrés.

Our family's journey to the United States brought a considerable amount of change. One of the few things that has remained as a constant is the love and friendship between Andrés and I. His passion and lightheartedness are just some of the many things I have always admired about him. He strives for excellence and is constantly breaking belief barriers; although, I believe the greatest gift that God has given him is his burning desire to love and serve people. Ultimately, that is what this story is about. This book is much more than our family's legacy; it is a narrative that gives us an immersive experience that allows us to better understand loyalty, compassion, perseverance, and the true purpose of family. It gives us the opportunity to gain a new perspective on the challenges that migrant families face and therefore reminds us of the importance of gratitude. The stories of the strangers that helped us along the way will give you an emotional reminder of how beautiful humanity can be. Regardless of why you decided to pick up this book, I hope that leads you to a renewed sense of pride and love for your own family. I know you will enjoy reliving this journey with us.

Julian Eduardo Gamboa Barrera

Being the only hispanic in my class back in elementary school, I felt pretty excluded from everyone else. Not to the point where it was noticeable, but it was definitely subconsciously evident. Being five-ish, I had nothing really to identify myself as besides my skin color and blood. I was proud to be Colombian. I would tell anyone who met me, I would always draw yellow, blue, and red any chance I got. If anyone mistook me for a Mexican, I would arrogantly correct them.

As I got older and grew out of my childish ways, my views on my ancestry slowly morphed. When I reached my teenage years, I would hear about how my family crossed the border. They would reminisce together about those times, while I was left completely out of the loop. It was like an inside joke you didn't—and would never—understand. The exclusion that I had felt at school during my early years then followed me into my family life, and it didn't help that I was the youngest by eight or so years.

When I was thirteen, we took a trip to Colombia. It was my first time seeing the country in person. It was beautiful, while in some places decrepit. My relatives native to the country would often make fun of my poor Spanish at the time, and about the fact that I wasn't a "real" Colombian. Suddenly the thing I identified myself as for most of my life was taken away from me. Any pride I previously had felt quickly subsided. As I grew closer to my current age, I heard more stories about Colombia, most not entirely pleasant. Through my father and mother, cracks began to form in the once perfect image I had.

Today, having matured, I can look at my heritage with pride. The world isn't black and white, thankfully, and those cracks are easily ignorable. The exclusion I experienced through my family still persists in certain ways, but I know no matter what is said, and even if I wasn't there for the immigration, I know I can't change the fact that Colombia is in my blood. Hopefully, I can visit the nation again in the future with a clearer vision and appreciate it more than I have previously.

There was an eight-year age difference between me and my middle brother. My eldest brother Andrés and I have an eleven-year difference. Obviously, growing up, this caused us to not really talk much. I looked up to both of them a lot as a kid, but them being teenagers, I'm sure I was just some annoying little kid that happened to be their little brother. We rarely spent time together if my memory serves me right, so I always only hung out with my one or two friends.

As I've grown and stopped talking about whatever weird mumbo jumbo spews out of children's mouths, my brother and I have inevitably grown closer. When I was around thirteen maybe, he took me with him to Disney World with full access to all of the parks. We spent a day exploring the parks together and trying out the rides despite my protests. We really bonded that day, and it really laid the foundation for our present relationship.

Despite his definite flaws, I love my brother very much. Our age difference still makes it hard to communicate sometimes, with me being a teenager in the modern era, but that's okay. I am excited to hopefully spend more time with him once I move to his city in August for college, if he will receive my strange self. I will now stop typing.

Rodrigo Gamboa Mogollon

For me, the meaning of being a father is PRIDE, HONOR AND LOVE—a lot of love. My mother said something that over time I have come to verify: "Children are like the fingers of the hand. They are each different, but they all feel the same pain, and if one hurts so does your whole hand." My three children have filled me with pride. It is an honor to be their father. The three of them are so different from each other, but I still love them each in the same way and with the same intensity. I understand that each one has their own defects and virtues, and I have learned to reach them in their own way, thus allowing us to forge a bond of friendship. In my opinion, many people confuse the concept of being a parent with assuming an attitude of total dominance and authority. I have tried to follow the path of respect and honesty and I do not agree with the white lies that many people justify telling their children. It is not right to lie to a child or assume total control of their lives in the name of protecting them from danger or evil.

With my children, I have lived things that have marked my life. With Andrés I was able to experience the feeling of being a father for the first time. I understood that my decisions would no longer be solely mine because from that moment on, whatever I decided to do would affect the life of my son, and that is a great responsibility. I simultaneously felt the weight of that responsibility and the wonderful feeling of love for my son. This feeling filled my soul and made me feel capable of conquering the world and doing the impossible. I finally understood what my father used to say: "You only learn to be a son when you are a father." Unfortunately for me, it was too late to say I love you or say sorry. By the time Andrés was born, my old man was already gone.

At five years of age, Andrés was diagnosed with a heart condition where he had a hole between the two upper chambers of his heart. These were very hard months and one of the most difficult times of my life. We were constantly looking for solutions even when we knew that the only solution was open-heart surgery. On November 18, 1998, we celebrated another birthday for Andrés because that day, he was born again. I will never forget those moments when, being on his stretcher already sedated by the first dose of anesthesia, I asked him "Are you afraid?" and he said, "Yes, I have both fear and faith." I said, "Give me your hand and pass the fear to me. I'll stay with the fear, you stay with the faith. And he did. He went to sleep and just over two and a half hours later the doctor called our names. At that moment, I felt the biggest emptiness of my life because the operation was shorter than expected, but thank God they only wanted to let us know that we were allowed to enter the intensive care unit.

There he was, full of tubes and cables, his chest with hooks joining at his thorax, almost destroyed, but with that great spirit, courage, and maturity not very common in a six-year-old boy. The doctor gave him the nickname "The Old Man" because the very next day, he went around the hospital wing and talked to the children who were hospitalized and awaiting surgery, telling them that they should not be afraid of the operation. He showed great spiritual strength and a positive attitude toward the challenges he faced. He was calm in the face of difficult moments, almost cold, but above all, eager to help others.

When he arrived in the United States, he was a seven-year-old boy, and despite what many may think, it is not easy for children to adapt to this new situation, to a new reality. It was not something I wanted him or his four-year-old brother to go through. Having arrived months before they did, I had already gone through very difficult times but my greatest concern was them. The hardest thing isn't working a job that you have never done, or even the humiliation that you experience; the hardest thing is the uprooting process, forgetting at times who you are, what you have studied, forgetting about your past achievements, forgetting that you are far from what is yours. This path is what I call "the path of putting your feet in the dirt, the path of humility."

And so, Andrés and his brother assumed their new realities. They experienced hard times during that process and I am not referring to the lack of the comforts they had in Colombia. Material things do not matter; material things come and go. Throughout this experience, Andrés once again showed that same strength and character in the face of adversity, which has always accompanied him and has led him to many triumphs. Sometimes he demands so much from himself that he gets frustrated by his failures, making it hard for him to forgive his mistakes. I think it's all part of the passion he feels for what he does. This trait complements the love he has for his family and his concern for others, all of which make him a great human being. I am eager for him to share his story. I call on you to understand the struggles of those who left everything to come here and adopt this great country of ours, always giving the best of ourselves to establish our HOME here.

Everything that I lived through and suffered, I would gladly do a thousand times again, no matter if each time was harder. The harder it was, the more worthwhile I knew that sacrifice would be. I don't look at the cost. I only want to rejoice in the result, and the result is my children. That is why I feel that I am blessed to be their father. Each of them has been a blessing that has outweighed the sacrifice. Their dedication and character have made it an honor to be their father. That is the benefit I have received from all of this: to enjoy how far they have come.

Sandra Liliana Barrera Fuentes

The existence of God is proven the moment you find out that you are pregnant. The miracle of life is within you. When you receive the title of "Mother," your life is enhanced by the power of God. It is the best blessing any could possibly receive. I have had the privilege of being a mother three times.

You learn to be a mom without instructions—by trial and error. My first baby Andrés will always be my first. It is hard to believe that such a tiny baby is now such a big and mature man. I have always said that he was a unique baby and a very easy child to raise. He even spoke very clearly at nine months old and said, "Mom, I want a bottle." He had no teeth and could not even walk yet, but he was already talking. When I left him in his kindergarten class on his first day of school, I had my eyes full of tears, though I tried to hold them back. I cried more than he did! He, on the other hand, was very happy. He told me, "Mom, why don't you go? You must go to work right? Bye!" My baby grew up before I even realized it. He is still my baby, and he will be forever.

One of the most difficult tests of my life was when I had to give my son back to God. I had to give him back so that He may do His will. At the age of six, Andrés had open-heart surgery, which was a very difficult time for everyone involved. I had to trust God with my beloved son. It feels like receiving the most precious gift and then being asked for it back. This is where my insecurities were awakened, but with the faith that my gift would be returned to me even better than before and with a testimony that God exists. Trials like these test your Faith and generate a change in you. They help you understand the privilege that it is to have your child by your side. This experience taught me to always be grateful. It taught me to understand the struggle other moms who suffer or have suffered for their children.

Andrés was so brave in enduring the pain and throughout his recovery. He once again demonstrated his maturity. He seemed like an old man in the hospital talking to all the nurses and doctors. Once again, I cried more than he did! This is why I say that Andrés is a special being who has the touch of God! With his heart having been torn and sewn back up again, I knew he would have the heart of a lion, a heart that would give love, be brave, and have compassion. I always knew he would do something great for humanity by taking risks and making a difference.

I have cried with great happiness and pride because of the many honorable mentions, diplomas, and recognition that he has received. He has always been driven, making me the proudest mom in the world. His qualities and personality make him very special as a human being and as my son.

He has always achieved what he sets out to do! He was always loved by his teachers and participated in all kinds of school activities, including dances, soccer, and the school show choir. He is the best brother and friend anyone could ever ask for. He is loved by many. Andrés is the family comedian, diplomat, athlete, volunteer, traveler, cook, and speaker.

I have always joked that he is like my "Little Husband" as he is always advising me and giving me support. He seems to know everything; he is my counselor and my comfort when I need it most. Andrés, you are and will always be my baby.

PART 1

1

LA CANDELARIA

December 2015

We were just over thirteen years overdue in returning to Bogotá. Luckily for us, when it comes to closure, it is never too late to receive. "We will see each other again," she said, the last time I saw her. I had spent half my life waiting to make this journey back. However, I was certain that as she was nearing the end of her revered life, Grandma Adela understood we would return as soon as legally possible. She was right. These are the consequences that few people acknowledge when debating the politics of immigration over drinks. The consequences that are impossible to calculate economically or logistically. Consequences that immigrants deal with after being faced with unbearable choices in an effort to survive. This was my life.

The last time we were all here together was when we left over fifteen years prior. She was missing, though. Her absence had only been this palpable when she left us. I couldn't go see her. Now as I walked through the streets of the city, I realized that being away fifteen years was long enough to make me an immigrant to both nations. My accent, my memory of the city, and of course, my patriotism for Colombia were burning in my heart despite having spent so much time away. Nonetheless, I was out of place here, too; I was a foreigner as we walked through La Candelaria.

"All these colors are so beautiful," Rachel said in wonderment, once again reminding me of one of the many reasons I fell in love with her. She longed to immerse herself in my culture as much as I had immersed myself in hers. The colors in this majestic and historic district of Bogotá unfolded around each corner as we wandered on. Vibrant greens, deep purples and blues, and rich red variations filled the facades of the colonial buildings, the sidewalks, and the window displays. These colors distinctly symbolized the different aspects of the people, the culture, and the natural wonders of Colombia. It was as if the city itself was aware it was nestled in the mountains surrounded by the Amazonian jungle. Our tour guide, my tío Edgar (my mom's younger brother) looked up at me with the same curiosity and uncertainty I had seen on my parents' faces over the years after moving to the United States. A slight upward tilt of the head and a squinting of the eyes that unmistakably signaled the question *¿Qué dijo?*

"Que los colores son lindos," I interpreted with a smile. Thankful that Rachel was with me, I was preparing my mind and my heart to face the truth that none of us in the family had accepted for the last thirteen years: Adela was dead.

"Sí, claro. Venga les cuento la historia de Colombia."

"He wants to tell us a story?" Rachel guessed. "Your family story?"

"Almost! He wants to tell us about history." I replied. "You have a good ear."

"It must be all the *Narcos* we watched," she said with her ever so genuine humility. She turned to Edgar and said, "Dime." And so, I interpreted for Edgar as he told us the history of Colombia.

"When I joined the Colombian national police force, they made all of the cadets learn about this. Colombia is a country that is extremely diverse in its beauty. But!" he raised his pointer finger and said, "There is no question that the downfall of Colombia has been the curse of the two C's: cocaine and corruption. Have you seen *Narcos*?" Rachel nodded. "Pablo Escobar was a terrible man, but even before him, the country was already facing violence and turmoil. Colombia was liberated from Spain by Simón Bolívar—he is like our George Washington. In fact, the plaza we are walking to is the center of La Candelaria and it is named after him.

"Anyway, after our independence from Spain, the government was set up similarly to the United States but with some differences. For example, we did not separate the church and state. Catholicism has a political role in our country. Another difference is we did not have the same caliber of people in place to hold true to our constitution. That leaves room for corruption."

Rachel stopped a moment to take a picture on her phone of a *sombrero vueltiao*, a staple of Colombian culture. It is the *sombrero* of the farmers of Colombia, who are known as *campesinos*. This particular one was being displayed by a street vendor. Rachel made sure to capture the intricacy of its stitching. She always seemed to find beauty in places I often overlooked. She would find plenty of it here. At last, my goal of taking my future wife to visit Colombia was complete.

"I love you," I said.

"Well, that's convenient," she wittingly replied, "It would be lonely if it was just me."

"I'm glad you're here," I replied, smiling.

"I'm glad you brought me," she said as she squeezed my hand while intentionally pressing the ring that she had just accepted into my fingers as they interlocked with hers. "And you were right. This place is a lot like Asheville." It really was. Bogotá had a wonderful execution of urban and trendy. It has always been a hub for culture, art, and sophistication in Latin America. Yes, it was still a city in a developing nation and it was not devoid of its own violence and crime; however, despite the corruption, if you were to simply breathe in the air, you would know that the fragrance of a blossoming future was not just a dream but a tangible reality. It was no longer outrageous to compare Bogotá to a city in the United States anymore. The years were long indeed. The city had no shortage of food carts and vendors. They were practically in every corner throughout the city, but even more so in tourist areas like La Candelaria. It also had the liberal feel of Asheville. Different demographics could thrive here. Bogotá, it seemed, had developed as much as I had.

I continued to interpret for Edgar as we approached a corner where a large plaque faced us. "It was in this corner where the history of Colombia really changed. In the late 1940s, a very popular politician was rising in the polls. This was similar to Abraham Lincoln in the United States. His name was Jorge Gaitán." He said the last part with a tone that was quintessential to that of a Colombian national police captain. On the Uber to La Candelaria I had explained to Rachel that Colombia did not have different police departments for different towns. It was just one force for the whole country, similar to the state troopers throughout an individual state in the United States. Edgar continued, "Jorge Gaitán had enough charm to appeal to all sides of the political spectrum. In 1948, he was shot in this very corner. This plaque describes the decade and a half that followed his death. Basically, everyone took sides and the civil war started. This period is known as *La Violencia,* or The Violence." Rachel raised her eyebrows.

"Yes, very bad." Edgar said this in his English.

I kept interpreting as we kept walking. "That is really where the story of Pablo Escobar begins. The country had the perfect recipe for him to enter history."

"That time he actually said history," Rachel interjected, half guessing.

"Very good." I replied. I gave her a quick kiss.

"...which brings us to the other C: cocaine. As the war progressed, several military groups began to form. How would they be armed? How would they be financed? Cartels. The enemy of my enemy is my friend. Since cocaine was so profitable, it quickly became worse and worse for the country. And then what you watched on the show happened."

"¿Te acuerdas de esos tiempos?" I asked.

"Sí," he responded firmly.

"What did you ask him?" Rachel asked me.

"If he remembers those times. I think I might have briefly mentioned to you that he was part of the Search Bloc, that team of trusted cops that were put together to hunt Pablo down specifically?"

"Oh-oh-oh! Yes," she recalled tapping my forearm repeatedly."Wow, I forgot about all that. Could he tell us about that?" Edgar once again inquired with the aforementioned 'squinting-tilt' face.

"¿Nos puedes contar?" I asked.

"Of course," he replied on his own, overconfidently. I rolled my eyes. Rachel giggled. So, I continued interpreting and walking. "The first time I remember hearing of Pablo Escobar I had been in the force for four years. He had recently bought the soccer team Nacional in his beloved Medellín. We all knew he was bad news. But the guy was a smart one. It was really incredible how he got away with all that he did. It was movie shit. I was near here when this place was taken over. I wasn't in the Search Bloc yet, but I was downtown. It was 1985. At this point, Pablo was making enough noise to get on the radar of the United States. The biggest problem the narcos faced was being extradited. So, Pablo had a guerilla group named M-19 break into the Palace of Justice and burn a bunch of evidence linking him to cocaine. The Palace of Justice is like the Supreme Court Building in the United States. During the siege, several Supreme Court Justices were killed. Bombs went off and people panicked. It went on for hours. The National Army showed up. It had the classic markings of the reign of Pablo Escobar."

Before us was the Plaza Simón Bolívar. Straight ahead was the Colombian Capitol. To our right (due west) was the Liévano Palace, the building that served as city hall. Very French Renaissance. To our left (due east) was the Cathedral Basilica Metropolitan & Primate of the Immaculate Conception & Saint Peter of Bogotá, better known as The Cathedral. It is the seat of the archbishop of Bogotá and the fifth largest church in South America. Behind us was the Palace of Justice. Not to be missed was the absurd number of pigeons that wandered throughout the plaza, infamously amounting to well over two thousand; nor could one walk through the plaza without being approached by the famous homeless man. Daily, he would walk throughout the square without exception for decades. For 1,000 Colombian pesos (35 cents in USD) he would tell you a bit of historical trivia about Colombia. People would say that he was more credible than Wikipedia—or even most historians—and way funnier, too. This was due to his impeccable timing with profanities and borderline morbid gestures. In fact, it made for great television when reporters would interview him for opinions on current political news reports. Most people just called him El Loco.

"¿Quieren oblea?" asked Edgar.

"What is that?" Rachel asked me.

"Ummm. It's made with two wafer cookies that are flattened until they are thin like construction paper, but round, about the size of a pancake. Then, they put jelly and *arequipe* on it, which is a Colombian staple, kind of like peanut butter but minus the peanuts. It's made by slowly heating milk and sugar until it turns into what looks like caramel. They also put shredded cheese on it and then—"

"Sí!" she said enthusiastically to Edgar, "Gracias!"

Edgar gave us a few thousand *pesos* and gestured towards El Loco who was now ten yards from us and slowly closing in. I nodded and took the coins. I briefed Rachel on the identity of our substitute tour guide as he approached.

El Loco looked like he sounded. His voice was that of a chain-smoker of forty, coming from a charming yet scraggly white beard. In a way, it gave him credibility for the facts that he spewed. What he missed in teeth, he made up in idiosyncrasies that filled in this wonderful caricature, like water fills a jar of pebbles.

I gave him the coins and asked him to tell us a little more about the plaza while I interpreted verbatim, at least as best I could.

"Due to the nearly insurmountable corruption by the greedy assholes who serve in the Colombian Congress, our beautiful country is impeded from thriving as it should. We are a proud people. Currently, we are nearing the end of a civil war that has cost Colombia over 220,000 lives and spanned over five decades. As Colombia has economically developed since the swift dismantling of the fucking Revolutionary Armed Forces of Colombia, also known in Spanish as FARC, the country has been paving the way for other South American cities. There is talk of the construction of an electric railway in an effort to improve the current TransMilenio."

"That is similar to an electric train," I explained. "It is similar to a bus but longer. Also, it runs throughout the main roads of the city but it has a lane exclusively for its own transit. They would probably place the tracks of the electric train along the lanes where the TransMilenio currently runs."

"Oh cool!"

"I'll point it out to you on our drive to the apartment." The thought of going back to Grandma Adela's apartment fueled my anxiety toward facing the real purpose for our visit.

El Loco continued and I quickly caught up with him to translate: "Now if only the oversized testicle we have for a mayor would stop embezzling the fucking money, shit would improve considerably quick."

I handed him some more coins.

"¿Nos puedes contar de la muerte de Pablo Escobar, por favor?" I asked. He nodded.

"That *jueputa* Pablo Escobar died on December 2, 1993, a day after his birthday. His family was his prime weakness. He had been on the phone with them the day before, and the gringos assisted the Search Bloc to triangulate the signal. Pure Big Brother shit. Pablo died in the rooftops of his beloved Medellín. Some still love and worship him to this day. It is, however, to be remembered that there is no doubt that Pablo is the anus of Colombian history. Years after his death, Colombia struggled to stabilize. There was another cartel that quietly took over the business."

"Cali?" Rachel asked.

"That's right," I replied. She loved that show.

"¡Muy bien! Esta gringuita es bien pila," said El Loco.

"Pila is slang for clever or smart," I explained. I continued to interpret El Loco's words: "Cali was a problem, but what the show doesn't tell you is about the growth in numbers and weapons of the guerrilla. FARC became just as dangerous as any cartel had ever been. Thanks to the fucking dictator next door, they were able to take advantage of the situation with Cali. Just beautiful. We had it down to our throat on one side and up to our stomach in the other." At the perfect stopping point, Edgar had returned with the food. We thanked El Loco and walked in comfortable silence for several minutes, enjoying the *obleas*.

Rachel was the first to break the silence. She came out of a deep thought and asked, "FARC? Those are the people that came after your family, right?"

"That's correct," I replied, offering an inquisitive expression.

"It's just that he mentioned all those people that died because of the war." She paused. "You've told me so many stories about you and your family; it's just different being here and listening. Would it be okay if you told me some of those again? I want to experience them again, but this way." She gracefully spun with her arm extended. While completing the spin, she hopped to face me, paused, and said, "Being here."

"Yes. I can do that," I said to her and to myself. There was a wisp of fear in my answer. She felt it with me.

We were thirteen years late to help leave my grandma Adela at her resting place; yet, it felt to me that she died the day we left Colombia—fifteen years ago.

The city, my family, and myself had each changed and grown.

2

LA NOVENA

December 2015

We did our Christmas differently that year. All of my uncles and cousins came together and rented out a cabin in the middle of the jungle. It was time for La Novena, or The Ninth, which is a tradition that practically every Colombian around the world enjoys.

The concept is simple: Each day for nine days before Christmas, family and friends gather to pray, eat, drink, and sing. Often, each night of the event is hosted at a different house. On Christmas Eve, the last of the nine days, the ceremony begins about thirty minutes before midnight. The prayer takes about thirty minutes to complete, so at midnight, we all open gifts and dance salsa late into the night.

We know who Santa Claus is supposed to be, but that is not who brings gifts; it's baby Jesus. I certainly was the person who told the other kids in my third-grade class that Santa was not real as the new kid at a United States public school.

Before we left for the United States, Christmas was always at grandma Adela's. This year it was at the cabin. It was a three-hour drive from Bogotá, located near the small town of Sasaima. The most peculiar aspect of the geography of Colombia is that driving more than three hours can completely change the climate. This is due to the changes in elevation you might experience during a drive.

Bogotá sits high in the mountains, but Colombia is on the equator. This gives Bogotá the perfect blend of low humidity and comfortable temperatures—rarely too hot during the day or too cold during the night. The occasional rain shower or cloudy days would sweep through, serving as a reminder to be grateful for the sunny ones. Driving about two hours in any direction will take you to a different altitude. So at the cabin, the climate was warm and more humid—typical of the far reaches of the South American jungles.

As each day of La Novena went by, I kept being reminded of how much I missed Colombia. The last memories I had doing this with these people were from fifteen years ago or further. Among these was the worst Christmas of my life. I missed grandma Adela.

December 1997

I looked up at my mom who had just told me it was my turn first. That is why I knew I was a good big brother. I had to be brave. Lead by example.

So, I let go of my mom's hand and my dad propped me up on the table. *Why were these always cold?* I started shivering. Everything about hospitals was cold. The rooms, the tables, the metal thing that listened to my heart. The doctor started doing the checkup. Then, suddenly, I could tell that something was different. Something was off.

After a few moments of hovering over my heart, he moved on. The mood had clearly changed, though. I could hear my heartbeat. He abruptly stopped, and told me I was done. He turned to Danny, kindly smiled and said, "Your turn!" I looked over and Danny—along with my parents—looked mortified.

Danny then bravely stepped forward.

"Is everything okay?" my dad asked.

"Well, he has a murmur. It's a little more apparent than I would like for a five-year-old," he said as Danny outstretched his arms upward, waiting to be picked up. My dad helped me down and then helped him up.

"What does that mean?" my mom asked, attempting to conceal her worry.

"It means I'm going to send you to a cardiologist. Murmurs are not uncommon up to a certain age. Andrés is just past that certain age. I'll check Danny too, but being that he is three years younger, it wouldn't be uncommon. The murmurs are supposed to close but some may continue into adulthood. The reason I am sending you to a cardiologist is because the murmur Andrés has was a bit more noticeable this time. There is no need to worry. Dr. Marquez is an excellent cardiologist. He will know what to do."

He didn't.

February 1998

According to the last three doctors, this man was the best cardiologist in Colombia. 'Cardiologist' was the biggest word I knew (it would remain the biggest word I knew for many years to come).

He finally had entered his office after we waited for (what felt like) forever. His office was cold. Dr. Fonseca was a tall man. My dad looked little next to him.

"Mr. Gamboa, Mrs. Barrera. Thank you for waiting," he paused with a grim look on his face. "I will say this as plainly as I can: Your son has a condition known as ASD, or Atrial Septal Defect. It occurs when there is a hole in the top two chambers of the heart. The heart is divided into four chambers total. The bottom two are called ventricles, the top two are called atriums. There is a hole between the top two chambers and it is a significant one. We need to operate soon. We will do as best we can with what we have, but given the size and conditions, I would say the operation has good enough odds of survival barring any complications."

I tried to understand what he meant...what this all meant. But then my dad began to speak and his voice cracked like he needed some water. My mom motioned me over, her eyes glistening from the wetness of her eyelashes. She picked me up and put me on her lap, hugging me tight. My dad struggled for breath.

"What's happening mom?" I asked nervously. She thought about it for a moment.

"Well, Dr. Fonseca is telling us that you are sick and that it might be hard to make you healthy, but we have to try," she said so kindly that I had no fear of the news.

I realized I would have to start wearing warmer clothes. We would probably keep coming to this hospital for a while.

November 1998

I.

Clínica Shaio was located on the north side of Bogotá. Five stories tall. A looming brick building with brick columns that expanded down the street, what seemed to be more than a soccer field in length. It felt like the lair of a supervillain but I thought it looked like a prison.

We arrived on a Monday afternoon. I would be staying, alone, for two nights before and after the surgery. I was six years old.

My parents talked to the people in white coats, the doctors. Then the people with white coats would talk to me. All of their mouths said one thing, and all of their faces said another.

"This is normal," one of them said.

"There is no need to be scared," said another.

"Nothing is going to hurt," said a third.

How could they possibly know? They hadn't gone through it. A few months ago, my parents had explained the process. They tried to be careful about it, but telling your son his chest would be opened so he doesn't die from his heart stopping a few years later was impossible to execute carefully.

So how could the doctors know? The more the day wore on into the evening, the more I began to realize it was their faces I should have believed. My parents knew well to pack my extra warm blanket. Hospitals are so fucking cold.

It is interesting what a child remembers. I often recall times I was really scared. This was one of those times. Nighttime had arrived and this meant my parents would have to leave me in the hospital soon, in a room with another child awaiting a similar future, or so it was explained to me.

I might as well have just died from this heart problem then. I had no memories of spending a night in a different building than my parents. The little bit of food that I was able to eat seemed to be wanting to make its way back. It was still cold. I couldn't move. My breath left me.

Suddenly, there was a voice from the bed to my right. It sounded like magic. Like the voices I would hear from the princesses of the Disney movies at grandma Adela's place.

"Just breathe," she said. Then she asked one of the most terrifying questions I would get asked in my life. "Is this your first time?"

It was as if the room changed from cold to arctic. The realization brought by that simple question: Even if I made it, this might not be the only time. I still was struggling to breathe.

"Think of something happy," she said.

I tried my best to follow her instruction. So then I thought of my mom and my dad and Danny. I thought that I had to be like Goku from Dragon Ball Z (a show that was the staple of most Hispanic children born in that decade). Eventually, I was able to move and my breath started coming back to normal.

"Thank you," I mustered. She was the first person in this prison who had recognized the reality of the situation. "What is your name?"

"Alejandra," she replied kindly. I could hear that she was smiling. "Welcome back. It is okay to be scared. It is scary every time. What is your name?"

"Andrés," I replied sitting up. She did the same. "How many times have you done this?"

"This is my third time." She pulled her gown over for me to see the truth of the situation I was in, deeper still. There were two scars running down the center of her chest, almost to her belly button. One was older than the other. I could tell because the most recent one was a kind of pink that was bright despite the low lighting. "They can't seem to fix me so tomorrow they will try again."

"Does it hurt?"

"Yes. It hurts a lot. Not as much when you think of something happy. So, do that a lot. You can do this!" she said enthusiastically despite the whisper. "You get used to the food."

"I hope so." I really did.

"You should try to sleep. Did your parents bring you a warm blanket?" she said in a tone that was offering.

"Yes."

"Good. Hospitals are always cold. See you tomorrow."

I was wide awake. So, I did my best to think of things that made me happy. I thought of my grandma Lisa and my grandma Adela. I thought of my friends from school, *Tom and Jerry*, and fried plantains. Yet no matter how hard I tried, the picture of the two scars on Alejandra's chest wouldn't leave me alone.

I was angry at the doctors. They lied. It was not normal. I should have been scared.

II.

By the time I was able to fall asleep, I felt somewhat better. I woke up the next morning to find that my parents had already arrived. I sprinted to them the same way our dog did once she was released by her doctor.

"Please don't leave me again."

"I'm sorry, baby," said my mom, genuine pain coming through her voice.

My mom always had a way of letting me know how she felt. In fact, my parents never lied. In hearing the sound of her voice, though, I realized that this was as difficult on them as it was on me. Worry was not yet a look that I was used to seeing in my parents, despite the fact that this worried look had virtually been constant for almost half a year now. I had to be strong.

"I know it's scary. I'm so sorry. Were you able to sleep okay?"

"Yes, the blanket helped. I missed you."

"I missed you too." She was trying as hard as I had ever seen to not cry. I had never seen her actually do it.

My parents' obvious fear actually helped. More than anything, I felt extremely alone here, and knowing that I was not alone in fear made it easier. It made it so that we were in this together, even though we weren't.

"Have you eaten anything? Are you hungry?"

I nodded, just realizing how hungry I really was. The second biggest issue in hospitals is that the food is terrible. I was hungry but it was hard to eat.

"Let's try to find you some food. Let me go find someone."

My dad squatted. "I'm proud of you. You are such a strong kid. I love you with all my heart, Andrés." He hugged me tight. "Tomorrow, everyone is going to come and say hello. Your grandmas and your aunts and uncles. They are excited to see you and to be here with you."

That also made me feel much better. It also was yet another reminder that this was serious. They were coming to say hello, but they might also be coming to say goodbye. I looked back towards the room where I slept to see Alejandra walking out of the room to see her parents. She was a little bigger than me. Her dad was overweight and had a thick mustache. His face looked soft and rosy, the kind of face that gentle, kind men have. Her mother was slender and had a pointy nose. She had Alejandra attached to her leg while she played with her hair, assuring her that it would all be okay for a third time.

After a few minutes, my mom had found some food. Still not very good. I was told the food was bland because there were certain things I could not eat before the operation. As I was eating, I looked up to see some nurses walk towards Alejandra with a bed. She gave her parents a hug for a while and finally got on the bed. They then rolled her right by where we were sitting.

"I met her last night. This is the third time she is doing this," I said to my parents.

"That must be so scary. Let's pray that she will be just fine," said my dad.

"Will I have to do this three times?"

"That is not the plan, my love." My mom ran her hands through my hair. "Regardless, you are not alone in this. We are with you just like her parents are with her."

I knew she meant well. I knew she was trying to be honest. I knew she was trying to make me feel better. In a way it did. However, there was no way for her to fulfill that. Not with the night I had just spent, and the three others that were left. It wasn't her fault and I did not have enough words in my vocabulary to describe the experience I was going through. Really, not one person did. It was something that could only be experienced.

Alejandra knew and I knew: we were all alone.

The morning also brought my last meal before the surgery. Alejandra was right. I did get used to the food. My family and I went for a walk around the neighborhood of Clínica Shaio. North Bogotá is what people would consider the nice part of the city. It was strange walking through a northern neighborhood. My parents both came from the south side—not the safest place in the world at the time. Regardless, the south was home.

"Someday we will move north," said my dad, hopeful (I don't think he knew how prophetic this was at the time).

His business had just started and things were trending in the right direction; I guess "north" was a kind of "up". My dad had the energy and drive to do anything. He was the upbeat one of the two. Always silly and goofy. I got that from him. Really my dad's side of the family had that about them. My grandma Adela for sure. He was strong; stronger than ever it seemed, all things considered. The best thing about my dad was that he loved Danny and I. He showed this constantly by caring for us well, being present, and (more than anything) being very open and honest about everything.

My parents had a way of explaining things to us in an honest yet appropriate way. In fact, he was about to display this quality once more this afternoon. We entered the hospital again. Went back to the wing I was placed in. Alejandra's parents were there, still waiting for her to come out of surgery. My mom had brought back some *buñuelos* for them. They smelled amazing.

As the time went by, my parents and Alejandra's parents chatted away, carefully avoiding any sort of remote conversation on cardiology, but an elephant as big as this was always too big for any room. And so eventually my parents found themselves asking questions about the process and what happens next.

"I'm so sorry, could you remind me of your names? I am terrible at remembering," said Alejandra's mom.

"Oh, it's no big deal. We understand your mind is all over the place right now, believe me. I am Rodrigo Gamboa and this is my wife Sandra Barrera," my dad replied. "What may we call you?"

"My name is Maria Rodriguez and this is my husband Jairo

Castaño," she replied. "Our daughter is Alejandra."

They shook hands firmly. Despite the good conversation, the tension was palpable. The stress was building by the minute.

"Oh yes, Andrés told us about her. She sounds like a lovely, kind, and resilient girl. Andrés said she really helped him get through the night. Thank you for raising someone so wonderful." They needed to hear that as much as my parents needed to say it.

They continued talking for several minutes until, finally, a doctor came into the waiting room. The air was sucked out of the entire hospital upon noticing the look on his face. Maria started to cry immediately because this was not the look she had seen the last two times. It was not hard to understand what the news was about to be.

Alejandra was gone.

III.

I woke up the morning of the surgery still trying to think of things that made me happy. Unfortunately, the image of Maria screaming after the doctor shared the news about the passing of Alejandra did not want to leave. Nor did the image of my mom crying with her. It was the first time I had seen her cry.

Dealing with death never seemed to get easier.

I had spent the night alone, so when I saw Danny standing with my parents that morning, the fear of what was to come seemed to disappear. He was pretty quiet but pleasant as ever. I gave him the strongest hug I possibly could. My dad squatted.

"The love for your brother is the most important thing you will have in our family. Don't ever forget that. Someday, your mom and I will be gone and all you'll have is..." his voice trailed off. He realized what he was saying might not be true and started to tear up. We both knew what was at stake today. "I love you boys." He hugged us tight and cried softly.

My mom walked over to us and embraced us. We stayed like that for a while. I wasn't afraid anymore.

My aunts and uncles started showing up some minutes later, but by that time I knew that, I was ready for whatever outcome today had in store so the greetings were welcome. Finally, out of the corner came my grandmas. They were two distinct ladies despite having very similar stories. They had both lost their husbands while they had their children still at home. Grandma Lisa lost my grandpa when my mom was only thirteen years old, the oldest, with tío Edgar being her only brother. Grandma Adela lost her husband when my tía Ana was twenty-two, also the oldest. My tío Joaquín was twenty, and my dad was seventeen.

Grandma Lisa was successful in raising her children. Both my mom and tío Edgar were successful in their careers. She had also made savvy business decisions and had come into some wealth. She wore high-end clothes and was seldom seen out with anything but her classiest option for that particular day in that particular place. It was never obnoxious; it was classy. The creed from this side of the family was, "Hard work alone can get you anywhere and respect is yours to earn." Grandma Lisa taught her children to know their worth and to not let anyone stop you from accomplishing your goals. She walked and talked her philosophy every day. Despite occasionally losing sight of her humility, she was one of the most unassuming people I knew. She came from nothing. One of Grandma Lisa's most interesting characteristics is that she wasn't too devout in any religion but when she needed to, she prayed to her *Virgencita Maria,* a picture of the Virgin Mary that she had from her small hometown in the fields of Colombia. Today was no exception. As soon as she saw me, the tears started streaming down her face and she just hugged me.

"My boy," she said with despair as she ran her fingers through my hair. This was a good day to cry.

I wouldn't.

Grandma Adela's side of the family had a different creed: joy. A separate but equally wise way to live. She taught her children to learn to find the joy in life. There was gratitude that came with the joy. She taught the importance of living each day to the fullest, to follow your heart, because even if it was wrong, you learned while enjoying the moment. Grandma Adela believed that good and bad rarely came alone, and that they were worth the other; and at the end of the day, what mattered was that you loved others. She found the humor in everything; sometimes it was vulgar. Every aspect of her life deeply radiated this mentality, and it was infectious. Her anger would appear exclusively to stop my dad from letting his temper get the best of him. Her strength was her love. Grandma Adela was loved. Not just by her family, but by her community. She was a God-fearing woman, always preaching about having trust in the fact that God knows how He does His things. Today was no exception.

"How are you, mijo?" she asked as I hugged her next. She seemed to be the only one to notice I was extremely calm. I got my ability to sense other people's feelings from her. My confidence was her confidence and so she accepted this situation as I did.

"I'm good," I responded truthfully. I was ready.

Some minutes later, the nurses came around the corner with an empty hospital bed. My mom and I were the only ones not crying. Again, she was trying her best not to, thinking she had to be brave for me. After a very long hug among my mom, my dad, Danny, and myself, I got on the bed. As I rolled away, the nurses kept up with the inaccuracies of what I was about to experience. They just couldn't possibly know, and that wasn't their fault.

This was now between me and God.

I was rolled into a room that somehow was even colder than the rest of the hospital. The doctor asked me how I was doing and if I had any questions. I responded that I didn't and he smiled under his mask. He had been a kind man since he diagnosed me in February.

"Look to your right. Do you see that red button?" he asked. I nodded. "Press that for me."

I reached out my right hand over a red button the size of my fist. I pressed as hard as I could. Within moments the room started to drift away. They had told me that I would be asleep for the whole thing, but I was not expecting to fall asleep this fast. The voices disappeared around me as the room faded away.

A final thought went through my mind as my life went to black: I couldn't feel the cold.

IV.

It is very natural to want to scream upon feeling what can only be described as the same sensation one might feel if a steaming iron was being pressed onto their chest. It is natural to scream, indeed. Which is what I tried to do. My throat was too dry to make anything more than a choking sound.

As I struggled to scream I looked down to see what was causing such pain. Running vertically down my chest, a blood-red scar was being held together by some sort of thread and some hooks. At the bottom, where the stitches ended, there was a plastic tube that I could now feel running inside me. I could not scream. My left arm felt heavy. It was wrapped in a plastic cast that had cables running into it. Some I could feel were just attached to my arm, others were going into my arm. I could feel them inside. I could not scream. There were two cables running into my body through my neck. I started feeling them frantically with my hand when a nurse came in with the smallest cup I had ever seen full of water. I drank the sip-worth that she brought. That was enough, though; I was able to scream.

I would have preferred death for what felt like the lifetimes it took the nurse to lessen the pain. Once it was manageable, I was able to process and come back to earth. Each scream became a sob as I tried to stop moving, thus making it hurt less.

Eventually my parents came in. They looked comparable to me. My mom was pale, and looked hungry; my dad had changed clothes and had a terrified look on his face. Both had been crying. Next, I realized it was daytime. Fearful, I looked down again. It was so disgusting. I was disgusted. It would terrify all of my friends. Then the cold set in. Why are hospitals so fucking cold? I could barely think about anything except for the pain. It hurt to do anything. I just cried.

"It's okay, honey," said my mom. "It's over. It's over." She kept repeating that every few minutes as she held my hand.

I really hoped it was over for sure. I couldn't imagine going through this again. Then I thought of Alejandra. She was so brave. If she could get through it twice, then I could do my best to push through it once.

"You have been asleep for almost thirty hours. It's Thursday," said my mom after a while. "Are you hungry?"

I didn't realize it until then, but I was famished.

"We are limiting your intake for now," said the nurse. I had barely noticed she was still there. She had been messing with different things all around the room. "For now, all we can give you is some fluids. Let me go find you some." As she said this, I realized how thirsty I was.

My throat was still dry and my voice was still scratchy. Once she left the room. I started begging my mom for something. There was some water left in her bottle so she gave me a small capful of it after I kept begging for some. This was a terrible idea. Within seconds of swallowing the liquid, I vomited. The expansion of my chest cavity as I involuntarily heaved brought back the entire sensation of pain I had experienced when I first came to consciousness. I don't know how it was possible that I was vomiting. I hadn't eaten anything for over forty-eight hours. The nurse came back with two bottled waters. Once I caught my breath, I was able to speak again.

"How long until I can eat?" I asked.

"We can give you soup in a little bit," said the nurse.

"Thank you."

A few hours later, I was able to eat some soup. I felt slightly better and fully awake.

"The rest of the family is here to say hello, if you feel like seeing them," said my dad.

I nodded, and slowly different cousins and uncles came and said hello. Their love helped me more than any soup could have. When my grandmothers came in, I felt the most encouraged.

Finally, two days later, I went home.

December, 1998

What they don't tell you before you have open-heart surgery (or even after) is the degree of change that you experience in your life. Of course I was told that things would be different since seeing the first cardiologist, but I was not expecting how much different.

From significant things like the potential of a much shorter life span down to the smaller details like how much you hate showers, or just being wet in general, for the months that it takes for the scar to heal.

During the weeks that followed the surgery, I learned to loathe several activities. Some more than before. Vomiting, showering, drying myself after a shower, wearing a seatbelt, dressing myself, undressing myself, laying down, burping, coughing, sneezing, sighing, shivering and going to the fucking hospital.

In Colombia, the school year ends in late November or early December, so I was able to just be at home and recover. However, this was more complicated than it sounded. We went to regular, weekly checkups, several times a week.

For the physical therapy, I was given a very special toy to work with. A tube about the size of an empty paper towel roll. A shorter, thinner, and more flexible tube attached to it, and a ball inside the main tube. I had different tasks to do, daily. I had to blow into the flexible tube and raise the ball to a certain level. Another exercise had me maintaining the ball at a different level, and another had me blow the ball out of the tube if possible. All other exercises varied from that. I had never dreaded breathing so much. I dreaded it every day. This all came to a climax the day I had to go get my stitches removed.

It was Christmas Eve. The good news is after this day, the constant pain would start to leave, the bad news was that it was about to be the most painful experience of my entire life. We went to the hospital that morning to have a checkup that was far from regular. I sat once again in a bed waiting for the person to come and start removing the stitches that were now a dark red. Some scabbing remained and a fresh pink was growing through. Every time I came back here I felt that there would be a doctor or nurse telling me that we would have to do it all over again. Luckily, I was still in the clear.

However, this time around, a lady came with a scalpel and a pair of pliers. I was expecting to take something for any sort of pain but nothing was offered. She was so confident removing the stitches that I figured it wouldn't hurt. I was wrong, but at least she didn't try to sugarcoat it like the other doctors. I just wish she had told me how much it was about to hurt.

She cut the first one, and that part wasn't any more uncomfortable than the residual pain I was under, but when she started pulling on the thread, I was made aware of several new thresholds of pain that the human brain is able to endure without dying. It was as shocking as discovering a new color, but as miserable as what literal heartbreak would feel like. On that day, the decades this whole experience took proved to be the most excruciating experience I would go through in my life—from a physical standpoint.

As the year had gone by, the surgery had made us forget about the success my dad was having in his career. This success would end up being short-lived, for we would soon learn that emotional pain has an even higher threshold.

3

EL ANILLO

December 2015

I could appreciate that Danny tried everything I did and then seemed to thrive at it in his own way, leaving his signature on it. He always seemed to have the kind of wisdom that few humans possessed. Danny knew better than anybody what his strengths and weaknesses were. Most people I had met barely knew their own strengths and were utterly ignorant about their weaknesses, myself certainly included. This quality about Danny allowed him to seek the counsel and mentorship of people who he thought of as exceedingly skilled in any particular industry, school of thought, philosophy, practice, or discipline; this was especially true when it came to those areas that Danny himself felt inexperienced in. Moreover, his aptly disguised intelligence allowed him to learn from these mentors efficiently and accurately. This gave him a splendidly balanced sense of self-assuredness and humility. And, of course, when it was convenient for him, he had this cunning ability to mask any lack of confidence. But out of several other attributes, perhaps kindness was the one that eventually became the most consistent in his way of living. Despite this, he treated the people around him with the default settings he seemed to operate on: humor, positivity, and tranquility. Danny's athleticism amplified his popularity while he explored adolescence in a high school in the United States with only me as an example. It carried well into college.

There was never a shortage of interested females on his phone, on his social media, or just while out getting a sandwich. Every time he entered the room, it demanded attention, though it was never intentional. Like the select few gifted with such a blessing, Danny carried himself with such swagger as to make it rare to find a photograph of him not displaying it—even the candid ones. These were all the reasons Rose loved him. Yet she married him mostly because, on top of all of his exemplary virtues, Danny was a man of faith. Danny was ethically sound, though not without faults. In the way a strength can be a weakness, Danny lived according to what his priorities were. This made him work diligently in certain aspects of his life and procrastinate in others. Infrequently yet unfortunately, Danny's occasional order of priorities confused those who loved him. This is the price he paid for chasing excellence. Overall though, I was fortunate to have such a person for a brother. It was a privilege to share with him these sorrows of life, and the triumphs they brought. Simply put: Danny Gamboa Barrera was great and destined for greatness.

Danny, Rose, and Rachel were all in the back seat, while Edgar and I were in the front. Edgar knew how to navigate the streets of Bogotá. Traffic was one of the things that Bogotá (really Colombia in general) still needed to improve. It was unruly, chaotic. Lanes were hardly even a suggestion. If there were three lanes, that meant that as many as five cars could be taking up the width of the road. Where it was slow, it crawled. Where it was fast, it was dangerous. Bogotá somehow has the worst traffic yet the best drivers in the world. Virtually every car was a manual transmission, and with the steepness of the hills throughout the country it was a miracle that the mortality rate of a vehicular nature was so low—regardless of how high it was. This thought was enough to make anyone anxious. Yet, that was not the reason for our anxiety today. Today was the day we were heading to Grandma Adela's apartment for the first time in over fifteen years.

September 1999

Danny and I were born almost exactly three years apart. Every September, we would celebrate our birthdays on the same day, at Grandma Adela's apartment, which was conveniently placed within walking distance of ours. Due to its proximity, we spent every day there. Before school, after school, and during school breaks, Adela's place was home to me, my brother, and my cousins on my dad's side; when our parents were working, we were at our grandma's.

Ana, my dad's older sister, never married and (as it is custom in Colombia) lived with Adela. The majority of the time, she worked as the branch manager of a national bank in Colombia. When she was home, she never missed an opportunity to share her taste in music with us. She had an impeccable humor, and a never-ending catalog of wild stories of adventures she had experienced in her youth. To me, Ana was without question the most charismatic person I knew. She was well versed in all manner of topics—a walking rolodex of interesting facts and outrageous statistics. Every occasion called for her valuable and challenging input. When a conversation walked her down an unfamiliar path, her simple demeanor allowed her to let others speak while she learned all the intricacies of a subject.

This is how she learned. Her ability was storing information; her skill was to recall it immediately. Yet more than anything, Ana laughed.

Most exchanges were filled with her laughter toward herself, a situation, or an idea. Her aura poured out an enjoyable ambiance that allowed others to forget their stresses and burdens.

This is not to say that she was never serious. Being an aunt, a sister, and a daughter were parts of her identity taken the most seriously; she seldom did the same for herself. This balance brought forth the love and care she showed towards her endeavours and her family, yet left a signature of her persona in the souls of those privileged enough to call her a friend. She would probably argue that the privilege was all hers.

"Happy birthday, my handsome boys!" she said as we walked in the door.

"¡Gracias, tía!" Danny replied. She was hugging both of us.

"Do you guys know what you call a bear with no teeth?" she paused, looking at us with a smile. "A gummy bear!"

We didn't get it. But we still enjoyed a laugh because she did so at her own joke. "Why did Maria fall off the swing?" A shorter pause this time. "Because she didn't have any arms!"

"Ana!" my dad said trying to hold back his laughter.

"Knock, knock!" she said looking at him.

"Who's there?" he replied.

"Not Maria!"

We all laughed heavily as we walked into the living room. I would remember this place as much bigger later on. As we took our coats off, I could smell the familiar and delightful aroma of Grandma Adela's cooking. Any remote skills that I have, I learned from her. I went into the kitchen and said hello.

"Hello, my *calados!*" she said.

Calados are a kind of Colombian salt cracker. Each is about the size and shape of a teacup saucer. They go well in soups, and they are perfect for digging into a tasty dip. My nickname came from the fact that my ears were cartoonishly huge. (Luckily I grew into them, I think.) My favorite nickname however was Piolín, or Tweety Bird, due to the size of my eyes.

"What are you making, Grandma?" I asked.

"Ajiaco!" she replied. An iconic Colombian soup. (Look it up.)

My aunt called me from the TV room. I got a kiss on the forehead from Adela and moseyed my way to find Ana looking at me with excitement.

The TV room was my favorite part of going to Grandma Adela's. Another benefit of Ana living there was that she could take care of Adela. Almost every single day that we were there, we watched a Disney movie after doing our homework. I loved discovering these fantastic stories with Ana and Adela's humor playing in the background. We became enthralled with these nights, where the horror and the pain seemed to be at bay.

That TV room felt like the safest place in Colombia. The majority of my memories of home took place there.

"I am about to change your life. Prepare to witness greatness at the highest level. I just bought a VHS tape for an artist known as Michael Jackson. He is one of my favorites. You have probably heard some of his music on the radio, but this is the first time I have owned a documentary about him," Ana said as she inserted the cassette tape into the VCR. "Now, come sit and let's watch this. It is going to be a memory you won't forget." Quaint. My life was never the same.

On the screen appeared a man. He wore pants that were too short and so his white socks were showing. A hat that made him look like some sort of detective was placed on the curly, black hair that went down to his shoulders, at a tilted angle covering his eyes. Yet the most inescapable aspect of his attire was the single, glistening glove he sported. He seemed as dark and as thin as me. When the song started and the beat between the snare and the bass drum echoed, he began to dance.

Billie Jean, as I would later know it, brought with it the most legendary dance move ever performed: The Moonwalk.

For the months to come, before our Disney movie, my cousins and I worked on learning and memorizing all of the moves he did. My aunt Ana would record us on her camcorder. Those videos have to be somewhere in storage, but for now, they live vividly in my memory as the clearest and most joyful of them all.

December 2015

Entering the apartment for the first time after all those years brought with it a new layer of overwhelming emotions. Ana answered the door with her usual humor.

"What is up, guys? You guys get more handsome by the minute!" she greeted us, her arms stretched upwards asking for a hug. We obliged with our strongest of efforts. The memory of her smell was the only physical aspect of her that remained the same. She was so much smaller than any recollection I had of her.

Then, we entered.

The furniture had been changed and the walls had been painted. The space seemed a fraction of what I recalled. I stepped into the kitchen to find myself the only one in it.

The absence of the smell of her food left behind a scent of longing. The TV room where we had spent so many hours had now been turned into an office.

Where the fuck was I?

I could not comprehend how such a small space felt so vastly empty without her. After weeping in Rachel's arms, I composed myself along with Danny who was held by Rose. Ana called us back to the living room.

Out of the glass case in the living room, she brought out a glass dish with three objects. I recognized them immediately. They were the three objects that Grandma Adela wore every single day of her life for as long as I could remember: her glasses, her watch, and her ring. Ana then proceeded to take off the necklace she was wearing.

"I don't know if you guys remember, but Adela used to wear this necklace often. As she was entering her final days, she wanted you to have it, Danny." She handed it to him and he put it on immediately. "Andrés, for you she left this," she said holding up the silver ring. "Do you remember it?"

"How could I forget?" I replied. I took the ring from her and put it on the only finger it fit: my left pinky. Since then, not a day goes by that I don't wear it.

4

EL NEGOCIO

Weirdly enough, my parents had actually known each other their entire lives. They were from the same neighborhood. My parents both lost their fathers before they got married. They were fairly young when it happened to them. This created the need for them to step up and help serve the family, mainly by working.

Through this experience, they each learned to value having a good work ethic and constantly striving for improvement. Neither of them ever forgot their roots; on the contrary, both maintained their humility effortlessly.

As they entered their adulthood, their ambitions were valiant and their goals were hefty. The world was waiting for them to become something great.

Ultimately, they did not disappoint, but the journey certainly was as unexpected as the outcome and so the world had to wait some more. Life, as it turned out, takes more twists. It struck with an earthquake that shook us to the very core.

January 1988

My mom went to school for accounting and graduated with several honors. She soon was able to land an accounting job at one of the largest banks in Colombia. While pregnant, she worked her way up the corporate ladder and secured the top accounting position at the bank.

Her personality helped her. She made memories everywhere she went with anybody she encountered. Immediately upon meeting them, she made a person feel seen and known. To this day, every time she meets someone new, her eyes will be fixed, letting the person know that they are the most important thing in the world at that moment. Her colorful energy paints through her words and her warmth, causing those around her to completely fall in love.

At age of twenty, my dad Rodrigo was working on his degree from La Salle University in Bogotá, where he and my mom started seeing each other. By the time I was born, everything started settling perfectly for my parents.

At the time, my dad was going to school for business management and development. Always the entrepreneur, he was interested in new business opportunities and was born with an eye for potential. His weakness was his trust in his business partners.

My dad first tried his luck in the transportation industry. He and a business partner from La Salle had hired my tío Joaquín to work for their business. His job was to transport a load of cars from one city to another all across the country. Driving on Colombian roads, especially at the time, was not for amateurs. These are some of the most dangerous roads in the world, navigating one of the largest mountain chains on the planet.

Due to the history of violence and theft, trains were nonexistent and the infrastructure could not support air transportation; therefore, a business in road transportation was extremely lucrative.

However, to my dad's misfortune, his business partner turned out to be unreliable. He lost his share in that company through a hostile takeover found through some loophole in the finest of prints in the contract. That is how the story was explained to my little brain. I loved it when my parents included us in the "adult" conversations.

Luckily, there was a financial cushion for my dad to be able to figure out his next move. He searched around for the next idea, one that would be his own endeavor allowing him to create the culture and vision he wanted.

Finally, he realized that there was plenty of money in the production of construction materials, specifically sand. His business primarily produced fine sand to be used in concrete mixtures and other ventures. It ended up being located higher up in the mountains where the rocks were more exposed. This allowed for the crew to come by with their dynamite, blast the side of the rock, take the newly created chunks and continue to break them down into smaller pieces until they became sand.

From there, trucks would transport them all over the country. Needless to say, business was good. Once again, the business acumen that my dad possessed came through for us.

March 1997

All of this had taken place before my murmur was discovered. As the business grew, so did the size of the projects until eventually, my dad landed a significant contract.

They came on a Thursday afternoon when Danny and I were with Dad for the day. Their fancy hats and studded uniforms spoke for the years of service to our country as they asked for complimentary donations of materials to rebuild the base. As fate would have it, a government military base was located further up the mountain road. It was strategically placed to serve as a command post to fight the rebel guerrilla groups that were threatening to run rampant through the region. That month, a siege was attempted by the guerrillas, an attack that was several hours of gunfire and exploding projectiles. The government base survived the attack but were vulnerable for a second one.

The second attack didn't come immediately because the guerillas had taken a heavy death toll with their failed attempt. At this point, though, the highest ranking officers were still under the impression that they had to fortify the base. In order to do this, they went down the mountain to the conveniently located construction business my dad had built.

Always the moral compass, my dad could not refuse. In what became of our lives for the decades to come, this decision to help the government became the point of no return. My dad had just agreed to a donation that changed the lives of his entire family.

In conversations to this day, we have never been able to agree on whether that decision was the correct one or not. What was certain was that life as we knew it would never be the same.

Where this decision took our family is not something I would wish on anyone. Unfortunately, this story is not unique. Every day, thousands of similar voices are experiencing what we were about to.

My story is that of an immigrant family. It is a story of courage, sacrifice, violence, death, life, and joy. So, I recommend you buckle up and hold on tight. (The real shit is about to hit the fan for us. It is best to warn you.)

PART 2

5

LA GUERRILLA

With Love and Respect for Colombia

I was born in a paradise on earth located at the northernmost tip of South America. A country with culture as rich as its natural resources and a beauty that is represented by its inspiring landscapes, vibrant history, and its festive people. Colombia's people enjoy some of the planet's most exquisite cuisines, joyful gatherings, and sensual music and dances.

Officially the Republic of Colombia, it is *Colombia*, not *Columbia*. (This is such a common confusion that CNN had an entire article covering a Facebook campaign created to set the record straight. Some guy had gathered over 30,000 "likes" on the page.)

Colombia is a woman born with a captivating beauty, seemingly destined to suffer the extortions that humanity tends to inflict upon beauty. Colombia is a child full of optimism, joy, and a palpable potential for prominence, working daily to produce one of Colombia's many exports, yet equally as cheated. Colombia is a man dripping with the charming appeal of an enchanting culture of mystery and elegance while retaining enough self-awareness to recognize his imperfections. He wants to heal the scars left by a history of internal and external struggles with identity, self-esteem, sin, corruption, violence, and death, but he doesn't know how. Yet, somehow, Colombia is an elderly soul laced with a unique, eternal wisdom.This soul, however, is at times too fixed on immortality and the fear that younger generations will repeat the failures of history instead of its triumph. Today, Colombia is all of these things at once.

The tragic side of the Colombian coin, both literally and figuratively, became the corruption. The one aspect of a society that was not ready to be free. Colombian leadership lacked the altruistic mentality that allowed other governments to flourish.

Of course, as with most other Latin American countries, there was the massacre of its landscape, the relentless mining of its natural resources, and the egregious genocide that European settlers brought upon the people with its discovery. There is not as much as a mention of these extortions, crimes, and sins in common history books, especially not in classrooms in the Northern Hemisphere.

Colombia was founded barefoot, several strides behind the starting line, as well as with both hands tied behind its back and missing a leg. Few like to admit their own sins, so when it comes to entire nations, it seems more convenient to glue those pages of history together.

Our sins and not theirs, however, seem to be worth more dollars as stories of our people to both the media in Europe and the United States. There is no shortage of films depicting villains that are kingpins of some Colombian drug cartel, or a kidnapping done by some rebel group in the Amazon jungle. Victories rarely seem to last long for the old souls with eternal wisdom and uncommon fascinating tales. Tales like those of Nobel Prize–winning author Gabriel García Márquez. Our diverse music has been reduced and limited to only the sensual music and dances (that indeed are a gift to the world) of J Balvin and Shakira. As Colombians around the planet, we understand what role our country has to play. We serve as a country worthy of example when discussing a story of unmeasurable endurance, magnetic and joyful lifestyles, and the greatness of human achievement. People in this country wake up every day full of joy but never content with the status of their lives or their country. They maintain hope and cultivate prosperity through a species of patriotism born out of sorrow instead of pride.

Beyond the luscious emeralds, the legends of gold, and the celebrity of Colombianas exists a multitude of sacred treasures. Arguably,

Colombian coffee is the finest in the world. Colombia is the third largest producer of it globally. (I guess one could say that between that and the cocaine, we kept the world awake and going.) Colombia is home to the tallest coastal mountain range in the Sierra Nevada and has the world's tallest palm trees called wax palms—the national tree. The Caño Cristales is a river that flows clear and reveals the riverbed made of several vivid reds, greens, yellows, oranges, purples and more; it is thus often referred to as the "liquid rainbow". Equally as exotic and colorful is the pink dolphin that can be spotted in the Amazon rivers of Colombia. Colombia is second only to Brazil in being the most biodiverse country in the world, but it tops that list when you take land area into account, Brazil being ten times bigger.

FARC

As Adela used to say, "Good and bad rarely come alone." Therefore, it is impossible to share Colombia's greatness without also discussing the tragedy accompanying the glory. Perhaps one of the darkest eras in Colombian history is the time period associated with the following:

The narco-trafficking cartels and far-left rebel groups, particularly The Revolutionary Armed Forces of Colombia (Fuerzas Armadas Revolucionarias de Colombia or FARC) and The National Liberation Army (Ejército de Liberación Nacional or ELN), among a variety of other paramilitary groups.

In fact, there were as many as five major rebel groups in Colombia during the last two decades of the 20th century, each involved with one another and equally as intertwined with the cartels— sometimes as allies, sometimes as enemies. The common enemy, of course, was the Colombian government, and eventually the United States government agencies as well. To the west of Colombia, the Venezuelan dictator—and world-class asshole—was Hugo Chávez; he sometimes overtly, sometimes covertly, provided weapons to a variety of rebel groups. As the eventual fifty-five-year-old war raged on in the 1990s, one group in particular seemed to increasingly become a bigger player: FARC. Given the fallout of Pablo Escobar's death and a variety of peace talks between other rebel groups and the government, FARC started occupying the vacuum of power. Naturally, cocaine was extremely convenient for acquiring funds. Interestingly, FARC prohibited the use of the drug within members of their group; it was all about the money. Another fruitful venture for fundraising was kidnapping. The ransom payments paid by drug dealers and politicians, and then eventually the middle class, provided a healthy amount of financial support. This was enough to mobilize around 16,000 members towards the end of the century.

Since my dad's encounter with them and the years that followed, I have wondered what the odds were of the things that happened to us. That day was, in essence, the second domino that fell, and became the point of no return. It was perhaps just as significant as the first domino, for it created a chain.

June 1997

School in Colombia started in January. We did not have seasons. The weather was perfect all year round. We did have a break for a few weeks in between June and July. This break in particular I loved. It was the first time in a few months we got to go back to the business with my dad. We loved the big machines that carried extraordinary amounts of sand and sometimes colossal rocks. It reminded me of the strength my dad always seemed to have. And, of course, how could two young children not enjoy witnessing a mountain explode? We cheered as the detonation of dynamite sprinkled the sky like boulder-themed confetti. But most of all, we loved the drives to the place itself. To and from, we sang songs that were blasting through the speakers. Mainly they were old Colombian classics, but they were the ones that my dad listened to with his dad. Diomedes Díaz, who is the Colombian equivalent of George Strait, was my dad's favorite. Songs that spoke about heartbreak and love, death and life, and betrayal and friendship. Much later on in life, I would be able to speak English and Spanish. Unbiasedly, I can say that since Spanish is a "Romance" language, the lyrics of some Spanish-speaking artists are some of the most beautiful poetry ever written by a member of the human race. It sounds like the feeling you get when waking up on a Saturday morning next to someone you really love, even if the song is about loss. I fell in love with art created by words and would later be blessed with the mastery of two languages.

On one such day at the business, we were sitting down for lunch with my dad in his office when a knock at the door interrupted our conversation about who was the strongest character in Dragon Ball Z. My dad was the one who had introduced us to the show. It was a wonderful example of work ethic, honesty, and honor. Most of all, it bonded us to him and he loved that about the show, too.

"Good afternoon, gentlemen. How can I help you?" he asked the three men that had come into the office. Two of them were standing behind what seemed to be their leader. I remember thinking how odd it looked that they stood behind him, just staring at the back of their companion's head. Throughout the rest of the encounter, neither of the back two spoke. The only man who spoke had the oversized mustache and silver-peppered dark hair. Realizing their ominous formation, my dad stepped directly in front of the men and us. Danny and I knew immediately that this was not meant to be the friendliest of encounters. Everything about it felt off and the tension in the room seemed to skyrocket in presence.

"Rodrigo, we are part of the fifty-second and fifty-third infantry of the Revolutionary Armed Forces of Colombia. We come here in solidarity."

"What exactly is it that you are wanting or looking for?"

"We are trying to just establish a connection with you. This is in no way meant to be a threatening conversation. As it so happens, it is FARC and not the army who is in charge of these parts of the country. So, as a new business starts to operate, we just get curious as to the nature of the business that is now being operated in our territory," he said, putting special emphasis on the "our."

"I was not aware that I was violating any laws, seeing as how the laws are set by the government and not FARC". There was assertiveness in his reply, but the timid stance he maintained while still directly between them and us contradicted it.

"Well, the way that you seem to be making friends, I doubt it is difficult for you to pull the right levers with the government." My dad visibly froze for a second. "That's right. We know that some generals from the base up the road came and visited you a few months ago.

Ever since then, it seems there are a lot more of your trucks going up to the base rather than their usual route back down the mountain towards the city. We were just curious as to where your allegiances are. The Colombian government is a joke and a corrupt burning pile of shit. The people cannot possibly continue to let this oppression continue to spread like the cancer that it is."

"Everybody is allowed their opinion but I would prefer to have no dealings with you. I appreciate you coming in to see me, gentlemen, but I would like to continue my lunch with my children." He began walking forward as he said this. None of the three men moved. "I do insist."

"Of course," the man said with an emotionless smile. That was the first time I had witnessed eyes that were *empty*. He and I briefly made eye contact, and then he turned. "Let's go. Nice to have met you, Rodrigo." The other two nodded and turned to walk away. We watched them walk slowly to their car. They never turned around. The dynamic of our entire lunch had changed. The air of the room left as they arrived, but since they had left, that comfortable air never returned. I don't ever recall a memory of my dad withholding how he feels or why. This time, the look was not a worried one; it was a face of contemplation. A face common to that of a grandmaster of chess during a world championship. My dad came back to earth and finished lunch with us. We then packed up our toys and got in the car. That was one of the last times we were allowed at the business. I would miss all of the thrilling activities we experienced there. Even Danny knew something was different. For the first time ever during the car ride home, no music was played. There was just silence.

October 1997

I.

The last time we went back to the business was the week before Halloween. Since the encounter with the three mysterious men from FARC, the struggle for control over the jungle made the surrounding area (within a seventy mile radius of the business) into a war zone.

My dad began going into work later and coming home earlier, and never went on the weekends. He was still working with the army but on a much smaller scale and a lot less frequently; however, in the months that followed their initial visit, not a note was sent, not a phone call was made, nor was their visit encored.

We were on our way back from a trip to the tropical city of Flandes when the radio announced an attack on a prison where at least a dozen FARC members were being held. The prison was operated by the national police and was a twenty-minute drive up the mountain from the business.

"It is going to be too dangerous to return there," said my mom, a worried tone pulsating the air around her. "We have to move the business or shut it down."

"I agree," acknowledged my dad. I could almost hear the humming of his brain as it processed what to do.

"Do you have everything you need from there, business or otherwise?"

"No. We can't leave it all there."

"We are about twenty-five minutes from there," said my mom. "We might just beat the darkness. The sun just started to set. We can make it without a problem."

Without another word, my dad lowered the gear and set course for the business. Danny and I understood our parents were anxious. It was a look and sound that we had never experienced, at least to the best of my memory. As we continued the climb up the mountain down the familiar yet now estranged road, we began losing more and more sunlight. The ever-narrowing route gradually began to twist and turn more and more by the kilometer, one of my favorite parts about that drive. This time, however, I knew we were not driving up to enjoy it. The clock was against us and the road could become extremely dangerous. With news of the attack on the base, the safety of everyone in the surrounding villages had begun to be put into question. The region was quickly destabilizing and one thing became clear: this would be the last time we would come to the business.

By the time we arrived at the entrance of the business, we needed full headlights to see ahead. Reports of fires in the small area spread slower than the fires themselves. People were boarding up and some were turning violent. My dad ran into the office and we waited. A lifetime later was when he came back out with a giant cardboard box full of papers. He loaded it into the trunk and we were gone.

Through the torrential downpour of the drive back down was when we saw them. One of them was yelling at us on one side of the narrow road. The other was right in the middle of the road, not close enough to startle my dad but enough to make him stop.

"Hello. We just need a ride to the gas station at the bottom of the road," one of them said while holding up a big, red, empty gas container. "Our truck ran out of gas further up the hill." My dad looked at my mom.

"We can't fit you both, unfortunately," replied my dad. His guilt started to build. How could he not help these two farmers? They probably just wanted to avoid the coming conflict just as much as he did. So, after a pause he said, "I can take one of you. Would that be okay?" The men looked at each other, and thought about it. The man turned and nodded. "Get in. It is pouring. Son, please scoot over so the man can sit." I moved over to the middle seat, the man sat next to me, and shut the door. My dad began to drive. The man looked down at me with a hollow, friendly face.

I couldn't look away, and then he said, "Thank you for moving over, Andrés"

II.

The man stretched out his arm in front of me, to stop me from flying forward as my dad slammed on the brakes. "Rodrigo, drive," he said calmly, lingering in each vowel as he kept his arm outstretched. My dad obeyed.

"What do you want?" my dad demanded.

"Well, first of all. I will tell you what I don't want. I don't want there to be any bad blood between us, Rodrigo. We don't want any unnecessary blood at all, in fact. The question is: does there have to be any? I think, despite our political differences, we can agree on that right?" he paused to wait for an answer to his rhetorical question. "Right?" he asked, slightly raising his voice.

"Of course." replied my dad.

"Good," with the slightest delay.

"What do you want?" asked my mom this time. A defiance in her voice.

"Sandra, if I wanted to fucking converse with you, I would have fucking said your fucking name," he bit.

My dad barked, "Listen you mother—"

"No, Rodrigo. Not in front of the children," he said as he played with my hair. I could hear the friction of my dad's skin on the leather of the steering wheel as he wrung it even tighter. "What we want is simple. Not only do you stop helping the government—"

"Why do you think I came here? I don't want—"

"Ah-ah-ah-." He halted, his hand making the gesture for "pause." "What we want," he began again, "Is simple. Not only do you stop helping the government, but you also manufacture for us, double what you were doing for them, per month. Starting in November. That gives you a few days to hire some extra help, and don't worry, we will send over some very gifted and motivated applicants. You can let me off here." My dad pulled over immediately. The child lock was on. My dad got out and opened the left back door. The man stepped out slowly and they faced each other, there in the rain. "We will check back in. You better have that quota." My dad got back in the car and sped off. We never went back there again.

6

EL COPEY

My dad drove straight to my tío Edgar's place. Nowhere else made sense. He had already been promoted to captain, this held a lot of weight in Bogotá. Edgar was one of a kind. It took an extra hour of driving through the worst traffic in the world (literally) because my dad had to be sure we were not being followed. Frantically knocking on the door, my dad was holding Danny with one arm while my mom wrapped her arms around me. Edgar opened the door. "Rodrigo! What the fuck is wrong?"

"We need your help." said my dad, still catching his breath after the sprint from the car.

"Come in, come in."

"The FARC are following us, Edgar," chimed my mom before the door even shut, "They are following us and they know our names!"

"What the fuck? Tell me everything right now," he replied, immediately rising to search for something. "Where the fuck is...?" he trailed off what was barely a murmur. He finally found his gun. He cocked it, and bolted the door. Then he grabbed his radio and spoke into it: "I need Fonseca, Vives, and Diaz at my fucking door, right now." He put the radio down, turned off the lights, and asked again, "Okay, now tell me, what the fuck is going on?"

"Did you hear about that attack to free the prisoners?"

"Yeah. The one by your business."

"Well, a few months ago, three FARC men showed up there. They just spewed some shit about their ideals, and wanted to act like they owned the place. They said something about how they knew about my deal with the army. Well, I started slowly phasing out of that deal and trying to figure something else out or just switch to a different business."

"Why the hell would you not tell me about this then?" asked Edgar.

"I honestly thought it was just some sort of propaganda thing. I don't know! I just thought they do this to anybody new to the area seeing how much they can get away with. I didn't know they would know about the contract or of any connection to the army!"

"Well then, what happened tonight?"

"Well then...tonight as we were driving up on that side of the city, we heard the news about the prisoners and figured it forced our hand. We went back to get some important documents. On our way back, they stopped us and are now demanding that I make them materials. They gave me a quota."

"And you came straight here?" asked Edgar. My parents nodded.

"We weren't followed. I made sure of it," said my dad.

"Alright, well for tonight you are staying here. Tomorrow morning we are going to go to your apartment and pack everything, and move out of that place. It looks like your vacation has been extended." He picked up his radio: "I need an E.T.A."

"Fifteen minutes, sir," said the first voice through the radio.

"I am six out, sir," said the second.

"Twelve for me, Captain," replied the third.

"Turn off your sirens. Attract as little attention as possible as you arrive," he spoke back. And then we waited. The three policemen arrived as they mentioned they would. It was sort of impressive, but my brain did not have much time to think about it as the instructions spewed from Edgar. "I want you two to stand guard for any fucking suspicious activity. And you, you are going to go with me. This is my big sister fellas, I don't need to tell you the severity of the situation. Got it?" They affirmed. Then he turned back to us and said, "I am going to be back within an hour. I need to grab some weapons. Don't go anywhere under any circumstances. Got it?" We affirmed as well.

Then he walked out the front door and the room was left quiet, with nothing but our thoughts and our memories from that day's events.

The next morning, I was woken up while the sky was still dark and star-studded. My dad was hurrying me into the car. I dozed back to sleep.

I woke up to the sound of my parents contemplating in silence. My mom noticed I woke up and I asked, "*Mami*, where are we going?"

"Baby, we have to leave Bogotá for a bit while we look for a new place to live in a different part of the city. Something safer and away from people like the man who got in the car yesterday." My parents never lied.

"Where is my tío Edgar?" asked Danny.

"He is helping us make sure that everything is safe for us back home. Some of his friends are people that work with him. Those people are also going to watch over us while we are on vacation and in search for a new place!"

"Does this mean I will have to go to a different school next year?

"Yes. But, that's okay! You are good at making friends," she smiled and it made it so easy to believe her. She had a gift for this. It is interesting what a child remembers. I recall being aware of the situation. I understood that for us, this was just the beginning. I would have never been able to predict all that happened next. These are the memories that I would end up taking with me for the rest of my life, from the challenges that arose immediately following that night to those that came several years down the line in all sorts of different ways. We switched schools and moved places within two weeks of that night. I loved it. The new apartment had so much more room and there was a pizza place right on the first floor of our building. We were not aware that the events of tonight would pale in comparison to the storm we were headed towards.

July 1998

I.

From then on, everywhere we went, we had one or two policemen with us. On our way to school or on a trip to the grocery store or the doctor's office. At first, Danny and I thought it would make us the coolest kids in school. It made us feel important at times; other times, they would be a reminder of the potential danger that brought forth the need for the policemen in the first place. As the weeks moved on, they became more like family. My parents would often invite them in for dinner or take it out to their car. These men were handpicked by my tío Edgar, but they were young. Regardless, they were picked because of their superior trustworthiness, intelligence, and grit. They took their job seriously.

Perhaps even more fortuitous was the fact that after the prison break just before Halloween, the fight for control of that area had resulted in more reinforcements for the army. Therefore, it was likely that FARC was not only preoccupied but also losing the fight. Furthermore, relative to other FARC targets, we were smaller fish. So, as the months rolled on, the worry and threat level seemed to dissipate, so much so that in July, we decided to go on a family vacation without our assigned policemen. They deserved a vacation as well. However, they were becoming such a significant part of our family and daily routine that my parents invited them to come. The only rule was that they relax and enjoy themselves as we went to Santa Marta, a lovely Northern coastal city. We all packed into the little car and set off to the most welcome vacation of our lives.

II.

The vacation was phenomenal. We enjoyed the best delicacies of Colombian cuisine with a coastal twist. It was pleasant to exist in that world at that time. It was the first time I saw the ocean. When the week was up, it was time to head back to our real world, which at the time seemed to crumble beneath us. As we began the long twenty-four-hour drive back to the mountains, the doom of the life that awaited us grew by the kilometer. Then, after having stopped to eat at a small town known as El Copey, we continued on the road to Bogotá before entering a long and generally straight section of the road. Then there was the toll. An interesting phenomenon of Colombia. The tolls charged an obscene amount of money for entry all over the roads throughout the country, yet the roads absolutely sucked. Besides that, they generated massive traffic. As was the case on this day for us. This would only add more hours to the drive. The line to the toll was only about fifty meters away (about five cars away from our turn), but the line had not moved for over twenty minutes. "Son of a bitch," sighed my dad. The cars that were heading in the opposite direction were also not driving past us, so this was a large issue for the operation of this toll booth. The person driving the car behind us became impatient, and decided to skip the line by driving on the opposite lane and passing all the people in front of him. As the car approached the front of the line, an enormous explosion shook our car. All hell broke loose as the fireball expanded into the sky and people began running for their lives. Behind us, a second explosion once again shook the car violently.

Our guys quickly jumped out of the car and opened the trunk looking for their weapons. As they frantically searched, my mom told Danny and I to not look and stay put. Finally finding their weapons, the policemen situated themselves behind the car that was parked in front of us. Some people were running for the fields trying to find safety. We were in the valley. Everything was flat and no shelter could be found within a kilometer. Then the gunshots rang. As people ran into the grassy fields to either side of us, the party behind the bombings were using them as target practice, and succeeding at an alarming rate. Everyone stopped immediately. "Return to your vehicles immediately. This is the Revolutionary Armed Forces of Colombia. This is a scavenger stop. Have your identification out and ready to be inspected. We are waiting to detonate a larger bomb when the army arrives. Anybody wanting to stop us will suffer the same fate as the fuckers who ran."

By sheer coincidence we were about to be found. They coordinated attacks against the army and while holding people hostage, they checked for people of interest to them through the radio. It was only a matter of time before they found us on that list. The search began at the back and at the front of the line. The policemen came back and joined us.

"Stay calm. We are here to protect you," said Vives. "We won't let anything happen to you." My parents did not seem as confident as our companion. They looked at the two of them with worry, a look I was still not used to. Suddenly, there was a tap on the window.

"Identification." My dad rolled down his window and handed the man his document. The man spoke my dad's information into his radio and waited for a response. While doing so he said, "The rest of you. Identification." Nobody moved. "Listen, motherfuckers. I am not going to tell you again," he said displaying his rifle.

"That's a yellow on that," said the radio on the man's shoulder.

"Say that again."

"Yellow. Yellow on that identification," confirmed the radio.

"Well, look at this. I am about to get some points on the board today." The man cocked his gun and our guys jumped out of the car and shot the man in the chest before he could think to respond. Then the shootout began. My door was still open and I could see Vives hiding behind it as I was ducking. Fonseca was on the ground, dead. A bullet came out of the back of Vives's head and his brains with it. We were alone.

III.

None of us moved for what must have been an eternity. In fact, I do not recall who actually did move first, I just know it was not me. My brain was not able to register the details of my surroundings. The very next thing I remember is someone yelling at my dad. "Show me your identification, you motherfucker. What the fuck happened here?" My dad gave the man his documentation and the man radioed it in. More FARC members could be heard approaching. The man speaking was thinner than his gun, or so it seemed. He was not the one in charge. The man in charge was the man who came into my view next. He began searching Fonseca's body.

"Holy fucking shit. This one is a *tombo*," said the leader out of the radio. His skin was white and his eyes were green. Not an uncommon thing to find in Colombia, however what was unique about him was his abnormal size. He had the muscular build of a bull. "And this one too." Then, turning to us, "Why the fuck are two policemen willing to die for you?"

"Boss, this nice little family is of interest to us." The radio message had triggered our names to be searched in their organization. "The name came back coded 'Yellow'. Supposedly there is a quota that this motherfucker has to hit or we operate as we do with any other family. We seemed to have lost contact with Rodrigo, here, for a few months now. No set orders as far as procedure but I say we kill this motherfucker right here. The lady looks like a nice fuck, and these two seem to be the age we like to recruit."

"Hang on," the leader said. "What the hell was the quota for?" he asked my dad this directly. An answer did not come. "Either you tell me, or I beat the shit out of your wife. So, I will ask you again, what the fuck was the quota for?"

"Construction materials they wanted me to provide."

"Why did you not?"

"I wanted to stay out of FARC business."

"What the fuck is wrong with FARC business?" said the bull, showing his temperament.

"We can agree to disagree." said my dad.

"You probably think you are some fucking hotshot. Fuck you. What the fuck do you know about the cause? Not shit." He got even closer to the car, "I say we just kill this motherfucker right now." My mom gasped, and started to cry, only the second time I had seen her do it. This was not a common occurrence in my life. When my mom cried, I knew the situation was as bad as it could get. The muzzle of the gun was kissing my dad's forehead as he held on tighter to the steering wheel. The bullish man had his finger on the trigger, ready to end my dad's life at any moment. How did it come to this? I have often thought that any normal story should start in the beginning, however, this is not a normal story. So even the first domino is just a guess. The only question that mattered now: Was this the last domino? Was this actually it? How much worse could things get from here? The floor was crumbling beneath our very feet and the places left to stand seemed to be pulling faster away from each other by the minute.

The radio then spoke again, "Enemy spotted! Get your asses to the toll right now! I repeat, enemy spotted! Everyone to the toll right now!"

"You lucky motherfucker," he said, and then sprinted with several others back where they came from.

"What should we do?" asked my dad.

"Let's try to get the hell out of here. They are all going to the front so they should be distracted for a while, right?" replied my mom. My dad followed her instructions. As we began turning around and driving the direction we came from, other cars started to do the same. Whatever was going on, it was now or never to flee. I turned back to attempt to catch a glimpse as to what could be happening, when all of the sudden, the third and grandest explosion filled the rear window with a tremendous view of this ball of fire. We made it back to the town.

IV.

Back at the town of El Copey, we reconnected and shared information with some of the others that turned around and followed our lead. From all the different stories shared, the summary of what happened was that the army was walking into a trap. FARC had left the third bomb there to detonate it remotely once the army got there and tried to defuse it. The first two bombs were set to draw attention, prompting the army to come as fast as possible. Upon arrival, yet another shootout broke out until eventually FARC started to overpower them. It was here when a squad leader of the army decided to push forward as swiftly as possible until being able to reach the bomb and detonate it with a significant portion of their total numbers dead from the blast, along with the squad leader. The remaining FARC members left and once the coast was clear, we drove back no longer with our protectors. We mourned the loss of Fonseca and Vives the rest of the ride home as it finally hit us a few hours later. It seemed as though there was no way to have a normal life anywhere in Colombia. This meant that our options had now dwindled down to a single one: We needed to leave the country. The time had come to make a choice as the imminent danger would be present as long as FARC existed. An unpredictable gamble. The decision was in fact made, and our days living in Colombia were now numbered. This brought forth mixed emotions in our hearts. Back then, even I began to understand. This journey would cost us our lives as we knew them and our lives as we wanted them to be. The future that once seemed so clear was now being filled with the very smoke that rose during those explosions.

7

LA EMBAJADA

September 1999

It was a cold morning waiting in line. The line wrapped around the corner of the concrete wall (that we were still too far from) that surrounded the colossal building. The seconds crawled by like years. "We are going to see Mickey!" said my mom in an effort to keep Danny and I from complaining about the line. Everyone around us had the same look my parents did. I would never get used to it. A look saying that they were holding on to the last branch of some tree of misfortune that we seemed to have been falling out of. The purpose of having arrived there early was to beat the line. Mickey seemed a bigger deal than even I thought, yet people didn't seem too excited to see him. We had waited in line long enough for me to sound out the words that splayed across the front of the building in enormous black letters next to the accompanying flag with stars: "Embajada de Los Estados Unidos" (the United States Embassy). At last, it was our turn to enter the building and I felt the warmth.

The warmth only came through temperature and not by friendliness. This place looked more rigid than a hospital. The line continued inside of the building but at least we could sit. "Mom, what does embassy mean?" I asked after I warmed up a bit.

"It's like a home away from home," she explained. My parents never lied. "Whose home?" I thought to myself but before I could say it, a uniformed lady approached us. She was much taller than my mom and just as beautiful. Her hair was blonde and her eyes were green. She sounded kind of funny when she talked. She beckoned us to follow her, so we gathered our things and followed her. A long, lifeless hallway lined with several doors loomed ahead. *Mickey can't really be here, can he?* We were on the heels of this angelic uniformed guide when she stopped at one of the doors, opened it, and showed us in. Another uniformed woman looked back at us from behind a towering desk with a pair of flags like the one that flew outside sitting on the edge of it.

"Why don't you go play with your brother, Andrés?" asked my dad. I grabbed Danny's hand and we began playing with our Dragon Ball Z action figures near the corner of the already too uncomfortable room.

"Where is Mickey?" I wondered.

As we played, Danny and I eavesdropped. *Could it be that this lady was going to take us to see him? Was she selling the tickets?* From what I could understand from the grown-up side of the room I began to doubt that we would actually see Mickey. I was expecting to hear words like "magic" or "fun" but instead I could only make out words that I didn't know, like "tourists" and "visa."

"¿Dónde está Mickey?" asked Danny. Now we were getting nervous. This didn't look like the castle we were used to seeing every time we watched Hercules or Tarzan. Surely my parents didn't lie. My parents never lied.

Finally, Danny got bored. He got up and walked over to the grown-up table. Grabbing on to the edge and standing on his tiptoes, he peeked over the table. "Mom, is this where Mickey is?" he asked. The room went quiet. The lady smiled for the first time since we walked in.

To my parents' relief she said, "Enjoy your visit to the United States. You have your visas."

January 2000

A trip to Disney meant long lines everywhere you go, I found out. It is interesting what a seven-year-old remembers. More lines, more signs, more crowded buildings. It had been a long time and still no Mickey. Just a visit to an office and a hallway, at the home away from home. Mickey wasn't there. But visas were. I was so confused. My parents never lied. In the front of the long line was another sign. It read "Pasaportes."

"Dad, what are passports?" I asked.

"Passports are like...books. Little books," he explained.

"What is a visa?"

"A visa is like...a ticket to Disney."

"So we are going to see Mickey?"

"Of course! Have I ever lied to you?" he asked. He never had.

We had just finished getting our photos taken. I made a stupid face on mine. The new school year had started and we did not go back to school that year. Once we had obtained our visas, my parents' priority had become to remain safe and hidden. We barely saw family, except for birthdays and that last Christmas. The time had come to finally flee.

8

"LOS VERÉ DE NUEVO."

March 2000

I.

My dad's airplane ticket was booked for March 7th, 2000. Two months prior, we had depleted the last of our savings. The ticket was bought by a concentrated effort from the family. My dad would then land in Miami and take a bus ride to some place known as Grand Island, Nebraska. I had never been to an island. Supposedly, the reason we picked that place was because my mom had a distant cousin named Fabio who went to college in a nearby town. The place was supposed to be remote, and more importantly, it was safe. Her cousin lived far from there now, but he was still willing to take my dad to his final destination after the bus ride from Miami, where, luckily, Fabio's parents lived. They would accommodate him for that night before heading off to Omaha. After that, my dad would be on his own.

The time had come for my dad to say goodbye to Colombia. How long he would be gone for remained unknown. This was a one-way ticket on a tourist visa. For us, it meant being put under extra security and an unknown period without my dad. This would be the longest I had gone without seeing him. The idea of a normal childhood had died with the business. What we had so far was a normal immigrant story. The courage of what my parents did could never be overstated. The airport. One suitcase. My dad squatted down to talk to Danny and I. His brown passport in his hand. It was a little book. "Guys, listen up. It is hard to explain, but you already know. There are some really bad guys who want to hurt us. So, we have to leave Colombia and I am going to leave first to make sure that where we are going will be a good place for us," he explained. My parents never lied.

"When are you coming back?" asked Danny.

"I don't know. But I know that in a little while, you get to come too! I will be there waiting for you," he replied.

"Where are you going?" I asked.

"The United States. That's where Mickey is."

"When are we coming back?" asked Danny.

"I don't know," he replied behind watery eyes.

My dad never cried. I was very young, but even I could grasp some of the gravity of this situation. Then came the goodbyes. Both sides of the immediate family had come to see him off. Some would see him for the last time. It can always be the last time, I suppose, but when my dad hugged his mom, she held him as if it was. They stayed like that for several moments—the best kind of embrace. I am glad they did because they saved the best embrace they ever had for last.

My dad then came back toward us. He kissed my mom and held her tight. Then he hugged Danny and I. We did not care to hold back tears.

"Please don't leave," said Danny. "Please just stay. We don't have to see Mickey."

"I will see you again. I promise," he replied. Weeping, he said, "I am so sorry." My parents never lied. So he stood up, and turned around and continued to weep. The grief never did quite leave his heart. He just chose to live on despite it.

II.

My dad had made contact over a phone call after his arrival at Fabio's parents house in Miami. After that, the calls came sporadically. A few weeks later, we received money. It was the same amount that my dad was making here during the peak of the business. It would be a while before I would learn the significance of exchange rates. Being wealthy, as it turns out, is also based on relativity.

For the months that followed, we waited for the green light from my dad. We went out less and less. We received word through phone calls of the progress he was making and the status of this strange island. One day, the call came that let us know that my dad was ready. Our time had come.

July 13, 2000

We found ourselves at the airport again. This time, it was our turn. Just four months earlier, we were saying goodbye to my dad. I turned to see my cousins, my aunts, my uncles, and my grandma. It had finally hit me. I realized how long it felt since I had seen my dad, but the clarity of this moment spelled out for me that I would not be seeing any of them for perhaps even longer than four months. In my heart, I knew it would be years before we returned. It was the first time the fear of not seeing some of them again settled in. This was it for me and some of them. So, I hugged them all. Adela was the last one. She held me in her arms. I attempted to hold on to everything. The smell of her clothes, the feeling of being loved, and the soft sound of her caring voice after she kissed the top of my head and said, "I will see you again." Until that day, my grandma had never lied. She never meant to.

They disappeared as we made our way to security. Once through, we made our way to the gate as directed. It must have been so wonderful to be a police person at the airport because they all had dogs. I wondered if they came with the job or if only people who owned those black dogs with pointy ears could work there. The dogs loved smelling around all the luggage people were dragging behind them. We arrived at our gate and when it was time for us to enter the airplane, my heartbeat was racing. I had never been on an airplane before. All I knew was that after we landed, seeing my dad was soon to follow. We found our seats in what felt like a tube of toothpaste. We strapped in and a few moments later my heart sank as the tube began to move. My mom opened up the window.

"Here we go!" she said. If she was anxious I could not tell. We watched as the airplane skated across the tarmac. It came to a halt for a couple of breaths and suddenly I was glued to the back of the seat. The humming of the tube began to rise in pitch as the flow of objects passed us at an increasing rate. Then, the roar ceased and the liftoff sunk me down in the seat cushion. My forearm burned from holding on to the armrest. Suddenly, we all bounced and tested the limits of our seat belts as the tires slammed back down into the pavement, testing the integrity of the engineering that designed the plane. The buzz of the engines descended in pitch until we halted once again, at the other end of the runway.

"Ladies and gentlemen, this is your captain speaking," said the airplane. "We have lost power in one of the four engines. Please remain calm. We are completely safe here and we are in contact with the control tower. We will be deplaning shortly. Our apologies for the inconvenience. There will be buses and vans taking us back to the gate where we will have a team ready to point you in the right direction for the next step. Again, thank you for your patience. Sit tight. Flight attendants, please prepare appropriate deplaning procedures."

The roar of complaints from every corner of the plane drowned out the sound of the instructions that the flight attendants were trying to share.

"It's okay, boys. Stay calm," instructed my mom. My heart was still attempting to slow down and my lungs were starving for air as my breathing started to normalize. None of us cried. The thought of not seeing my dad kept us too fearful to try and cry. As the minutes strolled by, the people in the cabin grew more impatient. Finally, the doors opened and we all exited the airplane through a yellow slide (so far, the best part of the airplane ride). When we arrived back at the gate, once again holding our luggage, at least a dozen people from the airline were waiting to talk to the passengers. They split us into two categories, people that wanted a refund, and people that intended to be on the next flight to Miami. The latter was the smaller group, luckily for us. (The airline was offering a full refund plus a free flight leaving three days later.) My hands were sweaty as Danny and my mom were holding each of them firmly. Finally, we were told that our new designated flight was on the other side of the airport and that it was departing in five minutes. El Dorado International Airport was not an enormous airport by any stretch of the imagination; regardless, crossing it in five minutes seemed impossible. My mom took the freshly printed boarding passes. Danny was only four years old, so my mom picked him up in one arm and began to drag the bigger of the two suitcases. I was in charge of the small one. We began the sprint to the other side of the airport. If we did not make it to this airplane, we would then need to be on a bus in the morning that would take us to my dad and it was impossible to know when we would have another chance.

As we darted through the airport, the suitcase weighed more and more in my arms, as did Danny in my mom's. We rounded the corner and at the very end of the terminal I could make out blue-lit numbers signaling our new gate. We were not going to make it.

"Andrés, baby," she struggled through her breaths. Leave the suitcase...I need you...to run, baby. Tell them I am coming...I will be right behind you. Run as fast as you can. Your dad is waiting. Go!"

I looked over to see the blue-lit numbers again. No fucking way would I miss this. I bolted. I felt as if I flew and as I arrived at the gate, I noticed there was not a person waiting to take our boarding pass. However, (I shit you not that this is true) I sprinted down the tunnel and before turning the corner to arrive at the door of the plane, I yelled, "Stop!" Once I made it to the door, a flight attendant stood with a wide-eyed look. "My mom is coming," I said weakly. My chest had not burned like this in a while. I caught my breath as a second flight attendant was now at the door.

"Andrés!" came my mom's voice down the tunnel.

"We have to see my dad!" I explained to them. "Please wait." The tears streamed down my cheeks. The scar on my chest kept reminding me of its existence as it singed. Finally arriving, my mom handed them the boarding passes and explained the situation. They said they thought we would never make it. This was a reflection from others that I would learn to get used to.

PART 3

9

MEMPHIS

July 13, 2000

I.

Once safely aboard, we were allowed to sit in first class given the gargantuan mistake made by the airline.

In fact, we got a seat immediately next to the mayor of Bogotá. My mom still has her autograph. After a successful takeoff, I was fascinated by how miniscule everything looked. The Andes sprawled through the Amazon green that welcomed the late afternoon sun. It reminded me of the back of an alligator. We marveled as the sun set over the eternal horizon.

"Ladies and gentlemen, this is your captain speaking. We are now beginning the descent into Miami. Please ensure you fasten your seatbelt and restore your seat back to the upright position. Flight attendants, please prepare for landing. The temperature outside will be eighty-five degrees Fahrenheit..." (What the actual fuck?) "...and the local time is 8:45 p.m. Thank you again for flying with us."

"Are you guys ready?" said my mom. Her nervous tone fit the vibe.

"What is the plan again?" I asked.

"We stay here with Fabio's parents, and then, the day after tomorrow we take a bus to see your dad! We are almost there."

It seemed too good to be true. Danny and I peered through the window as the lights of a city could be seen. Eventually, we were flying right over the orange glow of the metropolis below. Further down we went until finally, the wheels touched down signaling the safe landing. The roar of the flaps effectively slowing the plane was deafening.

"Ladies and gentlemen, this is your captain speaking. Please remain seated and fastened while we taxi to our gate. On behalf of myself and the crew, I want to thank you again for flying with us and hope that you do so again. Please enjoy your stay here, and of course, welcome to the United States."

II.

It is interesting what a child remembers. Line, signs, and buildings. "Where are we, Mom?" asked Danny.

"Miami. It's a big city," she replied, looking for a sign. She found it: "Noncitizens." We made our way toward that line. She was holding the three brown little books. I looked over to the other line, the line of people moving towards the sign that said "Citizens." They all had blue little books.

"Why are their little books blue?" I asked.

"Because this is their home," she said.

"Is this our home?"

"Not yet. But it will be our home away from home."

"Like an embassy?" I asked.

"Even more than that," she said.

"So we will have brown little books and blue little books?"

"Maybe. But it's hard to know right now."

"I want a blue one," I said.

"Everybody wants a blue one," she said. My mom was full of those moments of wisdom. Simplified so I would never forget it.

The line eventually split again. A sign that read "Colombians." It separated from the line of people walking towards the alternative: "Other." A person who I guess was a cop ushered us forward. Two others spoke and I could not understand what the fuck they were saying. Finally, they gestured for her to open the two suitcases. I did not need to know the words they were using to understand that they did not like us being there.

My mom opened the suitcase and they pugnaciously said, "Drogas?" elongating the vowels and sustaining the last syllable.

"No," said my mom sternly. The one seemingly in charge looked at me with a disdain I had not yet experienced in my seven short years of living. I reciprocated once I was aware of the swafting sense of superiority he put on. At least FARC pretended to be friendly. After more "searching," he threw both open suitcases forward and past the final checkpoint to let us exit the terminal. We helped my mom gather our belongings and folded them snuggly once again so they could fit. We made our way down the escalator and my mom recognized Fabio's dad. He was her distant uncle somehow. After a short greeting, he grabbed the suitcase from my mom and beckoned us outside through the sliding door. We were struck across the face by the wall of humidity that encompassed the air of the region. We were not in Colombia anymore.

The traffic in Miami was significantly organized relative to what I was used to in Bogotá. Everything was enlarged. The width of the road seemed twice the width of the streets of Bogotá. The cars appeared futuristic. Like the ones we would occasionally see in the movies. How could anybody be stressed driving in this country? The architecture was modern—and cleaner, as if someone had polished all of the buildings recently. We drove through the Miami streets attempting to grasp the vast alternate universe we were about to discover.

July 15, 2000

The Greyhound bus was an unfortunate and steep downgrade from the first class experience of the flight. However, the excitement and anxiety of seeing my dad again made the discomfort entirely forgettable. Further aiding in the oblivion of the musky air and destitute amount of cubic space, my mom told us stories about Grandma Lisa. Grandma Lisa, though way less rambunctious than Adela, was more extravagant. She spoiled us. It was a delight to spend days at her place due to the obvious joy she felt in seeing us. Of all the women I have known so far, none could repeat the miracle she executed in raising her children to become what they did while simultaneously finding success in her career.

"There is no need to be nervous. If I know anything about Grandma Lisa is that she always finds a way. We will see her again. Just you wait." My parents never lied. "Your grandma taught me to be resilient in times like these. She taught it to me by example." As the ride continued, we listened to the childhood she experienced. Through the twenty-hour drive we examined the stark differences in the landscape of the country we had arrived at. We saw the feats of even more architecture as we witnessed first-hand the skylines of Orlando, Jacksonville, Atlanta, Nashville, and at long last, Memphis. After thousands of miles and countless days, I was ready to see my dad. The change in atmosphere and landscape made it nearly impossible to determine if this was a nightmare, a dream, or both. The word "real" had lost any real definition for the rest of my life. The bus roamed the city seeking its resting place and our destination. He had to be here; my parents never lied. Anytime now we would see a station where he would be waiting. After two lights and a left turn, the bus station came into view. I stood on the seat. "Mom, I see it! I see it!"

"Where?" asked Danny. "I don't see anything."

"Right there." She pointed towards the emerging parking lot containing several dozen buses. The driver pulled up to the lot and followed the path to our designated location. Through the window I caught a glimpse of a man with my dad's face. The enormous smile protruding from the bearded man guaranteed it was actually him. I attempted to understand the physical change my dad had undergone. He was shorter than I remember, and unquestionably thinner. His jawline protruding nearly as much as his cheek bones. The bus came to a stop and we gathered our belongings. We patiently waited for our turn to exit. I reached the concrete and sprinted to him. He was much more firm, with a strength in him that I had not felt from him before. Danny and I held onto him all the same. He hugged my mom, gave her a long kiss as the tears dropped to his beard. He held us all until the driver brought over our luggage, and then for even longer after.

10

DAD'S PART

"Knowing how to give is harder than knowing how to receive. When you give while wanting something in return, you are not giving, you are buying. That is why I don't care if the people that come through here treat me badly or end up leaving. You can only truly give if you do not expect anything in return. If you give a homeless man some money and you care if he buys food or drugs with it, then you are not giving freely. You have an expectation. It does not matter how the person uses the gift. You have to not care what the person does with what you gave them. This led to the biggest lesson I learned when I came here: the lesson of humility. I think God sent me that one because it was the one I needed to learn most and first.

I learned that when you sacrifice something and then pay the price for that sacrifice, you have to pay the highest price possible; otherwise, it would not be worth the sacrifice. I made sure that it was worth it to me." —Rodrigo Gamboa

March 2000

I.

Rodrigo was on a bus from Miami to Omaha, Nebraska. Fabio then drove him from to Grand Island to meet with the only connection to the rest of Nebraska. They arrived on a Sunday evening at 9:00 p.m. It was the proverbial "square one." The first wave of culture shock came to Rodrigo through his first true experience with cold weather. As he would find out, while March was not the coldest month of the year in Nebraska, it still brought with it the frigid temperatures of a late winter. Outside waiting for him at the place he would sleep for nearly four months was an estranged friend of Fabio's during his time living in Nebraska. The man was missing several teeth as he smiled, extending his hand to greet my dad.

"David, this is Rodrigo. Rodrigo, this is David," said Fabio. "I would love to stay but my drive is extremely long from here. I have to get back no later than tomorrow afternoon, so I should get going. Rodrigo, here is your suitcase." He rolled it to where Rodrigo and David were now standing. He shook their hands goodbye, got back in his Camry, and started his long trip back home.

"Let me show you around," said David. His Mexican accent seemed exaggerated. "There are a total of thirty people living here, including you, with a total of five bedrooms. So you will sleep in the bedroom on the third floor." He picked up his suitcase and followed David inside. The house's principal characteristic was the scent of mold that lived with the (now) thirty men. It had a presence unlike any previously encountered space in over three decades—in a developing country at that. But, it was a place to rest his head at the end of the day, and for a disproportionate amount of hours. The kitchen was the only space in the house that resembled cleanliness. The living room was turned into one of the five "rooms" the house had and sustained eight of the thirty. One bathroom was used for the entire place. The walls had streaks of mildew running the entirety of the wall. The inside of the seat had less white porcelain showing than the various shades of brown and dark green painted onto it, despite numerous flushes. It was as if none of them had bothered to clean the bathroom, ever. Outside of the bathroom was a pile of toilet paper rolls taller than Rodrigo himself.

"We shit a lot as you can see. The shower is in worse shape. The hot water doesn't work," said David. "Your room is upstairs with me and three others." He started toward the stairs. As Rodrigo followed, he passed two rooms, neither with doors attached to them. The last one he peeked into before heading up the stairs. As he looked inside, there was a man with a lighter, burning the bottom of a spoon to melt the heroin he was about to inject into himself. The other five men in the room were laying in cots, foam mats, and old twin-size mattresses. His legs became boulders as he attempted to make peace with the reality of the situation. He thought of his wife and his children and, one step at a time, he made it up the stairs. His room was at the end of the hallway. Upon entry, he noticed the change in air temperature. "In this room we keep the door on the hinges so the cold air in the winter and the warm air in the summer doesn't seep into the rest of the house," David explained. "The window was shattered a few months ago. We covered it with a blanket and some nails, but the cold air still gets in. It is still cold here in March and sometimes well into April. I hope you brought layers to sleep in."

He hadn't.

"By the way, you owe $150 for rent."

"Okay," replied Rodrigo. He reached in his jacket and pulled out $213 dollars. His entire net worth. He paid David the rent and asked, "Where do I sleep?" He placed his suitcase next to the cot David signaled to and the one he would sleep in for the months to come. It was vomit-scented, so he opened his suitcase and put some of his dress shirts on the cot as makeshift bedsheets to mask the smell while he tried to sleep. He would not be in need of dress shirts for a while.

II.

The very next morning he woke up to find the house devoid of most of its inhabitants. Of course, the mold odor remained as ever present as the cold. He had put on as many layers as he could find. The people who remained were the ones that were under the spell of some drug. Not once in his life had he consumed any sort of drugs or narcotics; however, being from Colombia, he was not ignorant to them and the dangers they brought with them.

Priority number one that day: to find food with the remaining $63 dollars he had. Rodrigo stepped outside of the house, picked a direction, and began walking. After three blocks, he did not see any place that sold food, just more houses in the neighborhood. To his surprise, the houses did not look quite as nice as the ones he was used to seeing in Hollywood movies. They all had a front yard and were spaced out throughout the street. Some had white picket fences. One aspect he was not used to seeing was bare trees. Never had he encountered the look of an environment where all the plant life seemed dead. It was beautiful in its own way. Rodrigo had a gift for being able to see the beauty of life, even in moments like this. More than anything, he missed his family.

The bitter cold of March was more than his clothes could handle as the wind seemed to pierce through the very fibers of his soul. Being outside in the cold—just existing out there—hurt.

"What the fuck am I doing out here?" he thought as he fought the tears. As they reached his cheeks, they frosted over. "It is wrong that I am even out here. Yet, you chose this for me, God. How can I endure this?" he walked faster as the wind relentlessly wrestled him. "No wonder some of them are doing fucking drugs." He thought about the explosion at the toll. "No. No! I have to do this. I have to make this work!" His brain kept searching for solutions, anything that would make it all work. Suddenly, the thought came to him. "I'm going to clean that fucking bathroom." The house had plenty of cleaning tools and materials. He threw his anger and sorrow at the bathroom until it looked new. The hours it took him to accomplish his first win allowed him to exorcise the demons of doubt. Hope returned to him and the image of the ones he left behind returned to his subconscious. In several different ways, it helped him stay warm.

III.

Almost a week had gone by and so far the only person Rodrigo had exchanged more than two words with was the clerk at the grocery store he had stumbled into when trying to brave the cold. He had only encountered other humans back at the house, and they were either working all day or in their rooms high on the narcotic of their choosing. His groceries for the week had left him with exactly two dollars. He had not a single clue as to where to go for money. Soon enough, he would have to beg people on the streets. Streets that were empty due the cold and the lack of people in general in the small town of Grand Island. If he could not manage to have a conversation with any of the other twenty-nine men in that house by Sunday, his luck would surely run out—if he had any to begin with. Instead, what happened Sunday was not what he expected. That morning was the first decent sleep Rodrigo had in the last week because the temperature had risen to a comfortable enough degree, provided he was under enough layers. Hunger, on the other hand, was not something he had been unfamiliar with. "If I survived that, I will survive this," he thought to himself.

His suitcase had proven versatile. He used it as a bedside table and as a closet. He rose that morning determined. He could hear the sounds of birds for the first time since his arrival. From downstairs, the faded sound of someone in the house talking to themselves startled him. "Great, I also live with a crazy person," he thought. When he realized that the man was indeed not talking to himself he couldn't help but happily yell, "A fucking phone!" He raced downstairs. A man sat on the porch, speaking onto a wireless phone. Rodrigo just stood there, for probably half an hour while he waited for the man to finish, pacing, filled with the most hope he had felt since he got there.

"Do you need the phone?" asked the man as he put the phone down. Rodrigo was too stunned to speak at first. He then composed himself, paused, and smiled. "Hello, I am Rodrigo, and you?"

"Ivan, a pleasure to meet you," he said genuinely.

"Are you Mexican?"

"Yes, and you are Colombian."

"Yes sir," laughing as he did. It was the first time he had laughed. He forgot what it felt like.

"Were you the one who cleaned the bathroom?"

"Yes."

"Why?"

"If not me, then who?" he asked after a moment of thought. His mother had taught him this mentality. He missed her dearly. Being the youngest always seemed to carry a level of attachment distinct from those of other siblings. "If not you, then who? If not now, when?" she would always say.

"True. Do you need the phone?" Ivan asked again, extending the phone toward Rodrigo. He took it.

"How does it work?"

"Well, you have to get a calling card. You will learn to love and hate these. They can connect you from home, but they are expensive and will often rip you off. Then you dial the country code of, Colombia in your case, and you can type the number in. That is it."

Rodrigo realized the price of ignorance. Back at the grocery store, the lady offered to sell him a calling card. Not knowing what it was, he declined. Regardless, he did not know where to find a phone, even if he knew what the calling card was for. "Where did you get the phone?" he asked Ivan.

"We have always had it. It broke about two weeks ago. Today, I didn't work. I am one of the few that does not work on Sundays. I bought a new one with money everyone had thrown in. Don't worry, you don't have to pay anything. You are in the garden, *carnalito*."

"What do you mean?" asked Rodrigo.

"This country is like the Garden. Like in Eden," and then pointed north. "If you go ten blocks in that direction, you can find all sorts of sin. Drugs, gambling, and sex." He pointed east and west. "In either of those directions, you will find work. Maybe that is what you need now. But," he pointed south, "in that direction is where you will eventually go. You are an educated man, *carnalito*. I can tell. Most of us here can't even read or write. We will never go south."

"What is in that direction?"

"The dream. Probably God himself. But for you, a place where you can learn English. It is the hardest path but you can use your education. Become something great in the country. You are in the garden, *carnalito*." For the rest of his life, Rodrigo would remember this conversation. Ivan was right. South would in fact be the direction where he would find opportunity and God himself.

"Can you show me how to use the phone?"

"Well, you will have to get another card. I just used up all my minutes to talk to my children back home."

"How many do you have?"

"Four. You?"

"Two," he began to sob. Ivan just let him.

"It's okay. I know how you feel," he said. Ivan just sat in silence as Rodrigo wept on.

Eventually, Rodrigo composed himself and thanked Ivan and

said, "One more thing. What does *carnalito* mean?"

Ivan smiled, looked him in the eye and said, "It's is Mexican slang for friend, *carnalito*. Welcome to the Garden." They chatted for a few hours. That was the last time he saw Ivan. Everything was strange. The houses, the cars, the fashion, the people, the food, the weather. Then Rodrigo realized the only strange thing in this place was actually him.

IV.

Rodrigo decided to head south. He ate the last of his food that morning and was committed to walking south through the streets of Grand Island until he found what he was looking for. The temperature finally made it so he could walk a long distance with his Bogotá weather clothes. He found a coffee shop with a Spanish name and walked in, hopeful someone there would speak the language. There was a gentleman whose face was behind a newspaper, like a movie cliché, and a woman serving at the counter. To his delight, she greeted him in Spanish.

"Welcome. How can I help you?" she asked.

"Good afternoon. I was wondering what the cost of a coffee and a muffin might be?" he asked humbly, the two dollars in his hand were going to rip in half from how tight he was squeezing them.

"That would be $1.70," she replied.

He could have teared up from joy. Just as he was about to accept the price, the man behind the newspaper spoke up, "You are Colombian, are you not?"

Hearing the unmistakable accent of a *Paisa* (slang name for a person from Medellín, Colombia), Rodrigo was stunned. "Yes," he replied.

"Nice to meet you. I am Pastor Felipe Valentin," he said as he shook Rodrigo's hand. "Let me buy your coffee for you?" It was half a question, half a statement. "To go, please," he said to the lady, and then to Rodrigo, "Do you have anywhere to be? Or would you mind going on a walk with me? It is the nicest day today since October."

Rodrigo was glued to the floor. The dollar bills in his clenched fist would change color soon from the need of air. He could only manage a nod, and Pastor Felipe Valentin noticed that something more was at work here—this man needed him. Pastor Felipe Valentin grabbed the coffee and the bread, and nudged over to the door. Rodrigo followed, still working out the miracle he had just witnessed.

"Thank you," mustered Rodrigo, holding back tears. "Thank you so much. I got here about a week ago and I am completely lost. My family is back home and I have no way of contacting them, I just found out about calling cards today."

"Well that is a lot to handle. Here, eat some bread and drink some coffee, please."

As they walked around in the nicest weather since October, Rodrigo told him everything. After hearing the details of the journey Rodrigo had been on, Pastor Felipe Valentin offered to drive Rodrigo to his church. There he was given some more food, some money, and a Bible. The Bible was signed by Pastor Felipe Valentin. (My dad still has the Bible to this day.) After that, Pastor Felipe Valentin asked my dad a critical question.

"Have you found a job yet?"

"I haven't, no."

"Why don't we go find you one? Do you have a preference or would you be open to anything? I won't lie to you, the only places you will find work are meatpacking plants and construction, or some other labor-intensive job. Are you okay with that?"

"At this point, I will clean Port-o-potties after a League Final at the *Campín.*" (The Campín is the home of the Colombian National Soccer Team.)

"Ok then!" said Pastor Felipe Valentin, chuckling. "You are going to make it, Rodrigo." They went to Fonner Park in Grand Island, Nebraska. The place where live horse races were held. Here, Pastor Felipe Valentin had a connection to find employment for Rodrigo. He would make a living cleaning horse stables. All day. So, on Monday morning, he arrived before dawn as instructed.

May 2000

He was paid in cash. His very first purchase with the money he had given so much effort to earn was a calling card. After a week of silence, the voices of his family members broke the barrier of lone-liness to remind him of the toll it would all take and how the sacri-fice would be worth it. Then he took off on the bicycle that he rode to work every day. He had found it at a garage sale for five dollars. Mobility was a welcome guest, but as he was not familiar with the small city yet, he lost his way trying to find a faster route home. The day was miserably cold and his legs were beginning to go numb. He did not know it at the time, but soon his legs would stop wanting to pedal and take their last effort of propulsion before freezing entirely. His brain was conscious of its intentions but his body had refused to worry about such tribulations and focused on maintaining vital or-gans functioning—before the cold froze it all over. The manager of a small grocery ran out to find his motionless body on the edge of the sidewalk. She called for help and among four people they carried Rodrigo into the store. After coming back to consciousness inside of a humble store, he smelled the sweetness of hot chocolate that had been prepared for him. Once he thawed, he was given a ride home by a kind stranger.

A vehicle was the next step, but the bicycle would do for now. For the next two months he cleaned horse shit all day. He was able to send money home and even purchase a used van. Really used. Even-tually he was promoted and would now be feeding and maintaining five horses. He maintained as instructed. Two weeks went by and one of the horses trampled him, costing him his job. He was in bed for a week. This did not drain his spirits. The first day he was home to recover from his injuries, he received the news. His wife and chil-dren would land in the United States on July 13, 2000, with just over a month left to wait. Furthermore, he decided to take the job David had offered some days earlier. He would be packing meat.

Monday morning before dawn, he was in a van full of his room-mates. Some he was seeing for the first time. The location was a for-ty-five-minute drive that he used to get to know these men and their stories. Over and over, he was moved by the stories he heard. Some made him feel as if he had had it easy. As he thought about what his new job could possibly entail, he felt composed and was determined to work with endurance and vigor. The pay outweighed the stables heavily. What he was not prepared for was the humiliation he would face. After lunch on his first day, his supervisor had gotten word that Rodrigo held a college degree and was a successful businessman back home. This struck the ego of the supervisor and for the rest of the day, and for several months onward, his life was a living hell while at work.

"You fucking piece of shit. You think you are better than us because you can fucking read? Like the fucking degree makes you invincible. Fuck you. I hope your fucking wife gets shredded by those narcos," became the usual tone for the words of motivation the supervisor began the days with. (I will spare the rest of the comments that were said for the sake of censorship.) Rodrigo was not a violent man. In his thirty-six years of life, he had not experienced fury enough to contemplate murder. He had not understood that level of rage—until now. In that rage, he was able to realize the love for his family, because despite wanting to end someone's life, the safety and wellbeing of his family was the clearest thought in his mind. So he endured. Enough to rent a house and move out of the godforsaken place he had been living in.

His heart burst with joy every time he pulled a weed from the concrete or painted the corners of the rooms. He was making a home. He was going to make it. He saw that toilet that he had cleaned when he first arrived in his memories as he cleaned the humble house he now had rented. Unfortunately, as hard as he tried, the smell of urine could not be expelled. As it turned out, this would be the cheapest option. "Not ideal, but at least there won't be twenty nine other men doing all sorts of shit," he thought. He did the best he could as there were only a few days left until he would drive to get his family in Memphis on July 16.

July 15, 2000

The evening he was set to begin the road trip to Memphis the van did not start. He turned the key and the car refused to leave its slumber. He had not gripped a steering wheel this hard in a long time. David had enough mechanical experience to know the van would not move for a few days.

"I'll take you," David said after having been lost in thought.

"David, what about work? You work every single day," said Rodrigo.

"I know, but this is what I need to do for you. Any man who would clean that toilet would have earned a solid from me."

"How can I repay you?" said Rodrigo.

"Don't. But I do require that whatever this means to you, you pay it forward ten times over," said David. His eyes were as sincere as Rodrigo had ever seen in another man.

"I will do my best."

"No, no, no," he replied as he wagged his finger. "You can't let me down." He paused and gave Rodrigo a hug. "Promise me."

"I won't let you down, I promise."

As I type this twenty years later, I can tell you on behalf of thousands of people, Rordigo kept that promise. You see, my parents never lied.

11

NEBRASKA

July 16, 2000

It was just past three in the morning when the sound of the car engine stopped. The silence of the ambiguously late and early feel of the hour woke me. Perhaps it was my age, my memory playing tricks on me, or a mixture of the two, but the house I was stumbling towards seemed to be bigger than any I had seen up to that point in my life. My dad opened the door to let me be the first one in. More than the pain of my eyes adjusting to the living room light was the sting of the smell of urine, cigarette smoke, and protruding odor that I have failed to come across since the day we moved out several months later. For now, this was home, and though it had as much space as the last apartment we had in Bogota, it came with pets: two mice we couldn't catch during our time there and that we affection-ately called Pinky and Brain. The urine inhabited every part of my consciousness. As we explored the house, I came to find that it had not been furnished, not fully anyway. Cots covered by off-colored bedding created the place we would sleep, for a few weeks at least. This all was okay. Despite the piss, we were safe.

We spent the first month searching for furniture. Our third day in Grand Island began our regular after-sunset scavenger hunts. The sunset is incredibly late in the Nebraska summers compared to Bogotá which nests in the Andes.

My parents never lied to either of us even after we arrived in the United States. The weeks following our arrival in Grand Island, my parents kept us in the loop as to what to expect during the coming months. This was back during the days where we were still going to the library to avoid the heat of the summer. "Guys, listen up," my dad said as we all gathered around the floor of the living room. "We are going to be working on getting things for the house," he began. "Now, a—".

"Good, we don't have shit," said the four-year-old Danny.

"Danny!" protested my mom. "Watch your mou—" she tried her best to keep down the laughter that inevitably escaped. My dad didn't even mind. He was right. So, my mom picked up where my dad was so humorously interrupted, "We don't have money. So we are going to find stuff people are donating."

"What is donating?" I asked.

"They are giving it away for free."

"People do that?"

"They do here," she said. "The way it works is they take whatever they don't to keep and they put it at the end of the driveway."

"What is a driveway?" I asked.

"A driveway is those little mini roads that run along the sides of the houses and people park on," she replied, "And we can drive around in the van and stay alert for anything you think we need."

"We need everything," Danny chimed in again. He was on fire. We all laughed.

"Boys, we are going to play a game," said my dad. " Our mission is to find all the items on this list."

"Where are we looking?" I asked.

"Everywhere," he said. "If you see anything of the following: chairs, sofa, mattress, TVs, or anything that you want to have that looks cool."

"We are stealing?!" Danny asked, genuinely gasping.

"Of course not. Gringos are a little bit different. Here, people just put stuff they don't want anymore on the street, sometimes with a sign. If you can fit it in your car, it's yours!"

"Cool!" said Danny, and the hunt was on!

The very first night, we found a dining table and four chairs that are still in my mom's possession to this day. Some days later we found a large bed that the four of us fit on. Eventually, the house began to take shape and become a home away from home. I still wondered when we would go see Mickey, and asked my mom or dad. The reply was always a familiar, "As soon as we can." Of course the house had several faults. There were some leaks that would appear whenever a heavy rainstorm would come through, and the severity of these storms was such that since arriving that year I have yet to see it anywhere else. The hot water did not work, which was somewhat of a blessing in the summer and slowly transitioned into a curse as the winter came. The system that cooled that house was broken during July in Nebraska. A kind of heat that none of us had ever experienced before. Every time an imperfection around the house was discovered or highlighted, I realized that it didn't really bother us as much as it should. Small annoyances paled in comparison to the feeling of being in physical danger. In other words: despite the piss, we were safe.

While my dad would go to work, we would take our daily walk to the local library, where the air conditioning worked. We spent several hours of several days the rest of the summer at the library. Nicer librarians I never met again.

Another family tradition we regularly practiced while living at this house was delivering papers, early Saturday and Sunday mornings. It was one of these mornings that we first encountered racism. At the time, I did not recognize it. My parents had never explained the concept to me that based on my skin color, some people I met would think of me as a bad person, or worse—that I was less than they were. An old man was sitting on his porch, and it was my turn to take the paper to the doorstep of the next house. I first noticed him as I ran up because immediately he started yelling. I had not learned enough English yet to understand much of what he said. My dad had enough insults and curse words (that is what you learn first) in his broken English to understand that the man was racially profiling me. Even I could understand that he incorrectly assumed I was Mexican and only one other word. This was a word that I had never heard used to describe a person instead of an activity. He called me illegal. Frozen, I watched him make his way toward me masked under a face of anger and hate different from the anger and hate that had brought us here. It terrorized the same. He pushed me into the ground, reconnecting my brain. I sprinted back toward the van while my dad screamed at the top of his lungs the first English words I learned permanently, "Motherfucker! Son of a bitch! Stupid!" all from the choppy English my dad had picked up over the months of being here.

Delivering papers was not all that bad, though. It gave us a chance to dream and to set goals. While we were not illegal, we were living in the country illegally at this point. Our six-month tourist visas had expired. As we went to different neighborhoods to deliver papers, we realized the potential of the life that the United States could offer. A small town in the middle of nowhere still had what looked like mansions to us. We told ourselves that we would live in those neighborhoods some day. The income allowed us to upgrade from scavenger hunts to garage sale purchases. So, our house continued to be furnished. The stench never quite left over the months we lived there. Yet, despite the piss, we were safe.

August 2000

The only bits of good news that came on the day we enrolled in a school in the United States did not overcome the anxiety of the idea, but they indeed made me feel somewhat better. First good bit: No uniforms. The idea of getting to wear our Dragon Ball Z T-shirts to school sure cheered me up for a few minutes. Until we walked into the building, which was four blocks from our house, I could not understand a single word anybody was saying. All I knew is that as usual, there were more lines, more signs and more buildings. Second good bit: After several people struggled to communicate, the school interpreter finished assisting the family she was with. Her name was Ms. Maria Palomo, and she was much younger than my mother. Her voice was kind and her eyes were lovely. I couldn't resist blushing— she was so pretty. As it turns out, I would get to spend three hours per day with her to work on my English. (You be the judge of how well I did, as you are pretty deep into my book.) What terrified me was the other five hours I would have to spend on my own with zero friends, zero English, and zero knowledge of how school worked here. Third good bit: Danny was with me during those magical three hours. By the time we got home from the school, I had met my elderly teacher, Mrs. Morrison. Now it was time to wait anxiously for the first day of school.

Since my surgery, I had not spent time on my own with only strangers for company. However, this kind of terror is distinct to that of a life-threatening one. This was the kind of terror where you would rather die. The first day of school is always an anxious moment for any person. This was no ordinary first day. The only three people I knew within a four thousand kilometer radius (about 3000 miles) felt further than twice that distance. Again, I was alone. However, something happened on the first day of school that I did not expect: I made friends. There were three other children in the English class along with Danny and me. They were Mexican, and that made them just as different to me as my other classmates who were born here. Years later I would learn that some of my classmates that were born here either did not care to learn or did not actually learn that there exist stark differences in culture and history among countries of the same region or ethnic background. In other words, Mexicans were strange. It is interesting what a child remembers. For starters, there are certain words that mean one thing to a Colombian that mean an entirely different thing to a Mexican, or any other person from a different country in Latin America. I find new ones to this day. One of the worst ways I found an ambiguous word was when I used the word for jacket: "chaqueta." (I will leave it to you to find out what it means to some Mexicans.) Their food was wonderful. Every dish I encountered was a masterpiece—especially if it was homemade—yet the sting of the spice in the dishes singed my tastebuds. Or so it seemed. Their dancing was the hardest pill to swallow. No further comment.

All in all, Mexicans, Guatemalans, and any Latin American that I came across taught me about their vast cultures and history. It was a privilege to be surrounded by so many different ones in such a place as Nebraska.

A Short Love Letter to Mathematics

I can say with certainty that as a math minor a few credit hours short of a major, few things have helped me adjust to life here as much as math did. Mathematics was really my first language. It was effortless and grace giving. The first sign of hope I realized on my first day of school was math class, where my fluency in that language gave me a sweet advantage. It was more than I needed to succeed in my new environment.

January 2001

As the months rolled on, we began acclimating to life in Nebraska as best as we could. Later on, I would learn the benefits of the much more economic standard of living that Nebraska had to offer. Of course, the people we met along the way made it impossible to feel the need to move on too quickly as they helped us learn to love this place. As life began teaching us all so many lessons about ourselves, about each other, and about change, the latter came in ways we did not expect. One such way was the changing of the seasons we got the pleasure and misery of receiving late in 2000. In the beginning weeks of 2001, we experienced just how severely and rapidly the weather can change. Living in Nebraska would, in a unique way, teach us about adaptability—whether the weather felt kind or not. Winters here were brutal, challenging any neighbor within a thousand miles north of us. What made this unique more than anything, perhaps regardless of the season, was the unfathomable terrain of the region: the wind. Nebraska was flat. It must be stated that compared to the mountains, the flat had its own charm. For instance, since my years of arriving in Nebraska, I have traveled to more countries than I deserve and have been to nearly all fifty states; I can comfortably say the sunsets I have been blessed to witness in Nebraska are second to few others in terms of magnificence. The sunsets occurred on one side of the horizon typically accompanied by an infamous severe thunderstorm lurking on the opposite side. Directly behind you, the sky is dark enough for the eager stars to reveal themselves.

The same blessing had a curse: Nebraska was flat. In the summers, the wind made it practically impossible to enjoy a picnic or a sport. In the winters, though, the wind took its most excruciating physical form. It bit. The wind did not care if you were wearing several layers, if you were moving fast or slow, the direction you were facing, or if you were behind shelter. It found a way. The definition of the phrase, "You can run but you can't hide." The winds of winter significantly changed the temperature. It was in Nebraska that we learned that just because the thermometer says it is a certain degree of temperature (in fucking Fahrenheit) that the wind can make it so it "feels" like a much lower degree. Some days as much as thirty to forty degrees lower than the temperature on the thermometer.

Such was the case on a January morning while we were walking to school. It was my mom, my brother, and myself taking the usual walk of no more than five blocks. My mom had just come out of the shower, dressed herself quickly, and gone out the door with us in tow. Just from walking from the front door of our house to before we stepped inside a school zone (I shit you not), the hair on my mom's head had turned to frost. By the time we had arrived to be dropped off, the wind had aggressively frozen most of her hair.

That winter brought with it memories; it is interesting what a child remembers. The very first time we saw heavy snowfall reminded us again of the change and of the charm of our new home. The changing of the seasons broke down each year into a relatively shorter, and thus faster, sensation of the passing of time. The first heavy snowfall signaled the realization of how thick we were into winter. Our neighbors tried to warn us, in their kind attempts, of the forecast. The day it fell is a day none of us will ever forget. At first, it felt like entering into the universe of *The Matrix*. Snow had yet to stick to the ground so it seemed like rain, but slowed down and painted in white. In a windless snowfall, the flakes fell like feathers, and gently kissed me as they melted on my skin. Gradually, the snow began to stick and the world seemed as if God had spray-painted the earth in white powder (kind of ironic). This continued for hours. Next came what would become my favorite part of snowy, windless days: the morning after. Early on the next morning, we stepped outside to meet the sunshine that deceived us. It seemed like a warm day to the eyes, but our skin reminded us (in a different way this time) that we were not home. Cold remained. The snow had covered everything with thirty-four inches (ugh). To us, we had only seen this in the movies. We thought a scene like the one before us was just something out of the Christmas movies from the United States and were as fake as Santa Claus or Disney. No wonder why kids believed. With something as wonderful as this, we began to believe as well.

Everywhere we looked we seemed to find cultural lessons during our first winter. My dad learned and taught us the intricacies of driving in the winter, a task not for the faint of heart. We realized that clothing in Nebraska was more often sold for function first, and then for fashion—particularly for winter clothing. Yet, perhaps the most significant cultural lesson came both in terms of hilarity and tragedy. A moment so simple and peculiar that it defines the juxtaposition of good in bad. "Good and bad rarely come alone," Adela would say. The snowfall had given us our first of many mind-bending realizations. Now it was time to build a snowman. A task that would later feel so simple to me. They were impossible to miss during our furniture hunts that by now had become occasional. We decided we had to try. So, we started to put it together in a way that seemed the most logical: Put together a giant pile of snow, then carve out the shape of your snowman. Two steps. That simple. Three hours later, our neighbors came home and immediately realized what we were dynamically attempting to accomplish. In the clearest example of non-verbal communication since our arrival, Cecil, our kind next-door neighbor who was an angel during our time living next to him, packed a few handfuls of snow really tight. He then rolled over the rest of the snow and within minutes, he had a ball adequate enough to serve as the base of our very own Frosty the fucking Snowman.

With Love and Respect to the United States

"I pledge allegiance to the flag of the United States of America, and to the Republic for which it stands, one nation under God, indivisible, with liberty and justice for all." I had to say that shit. Every day. Imagine having to run and move to some country in Europe and having to pledge allegiance to that country on day one. Only a several million living in the United States can. The challenge of survival we faced once we arrived often seemed insurmountable. At first, it was a nightmare. It was obvious we didn't belong. My family settled in Nebraska where we were not thriving financially. We did not know the language, understand the culture, or have family. There we were. Lost in the world, surrounded by unfamiliar territory, drifting through life only wondering what was in store.

Yet, through all of the hardship and struggle, something happened. I did not know it at the time because it was not a single event or a sudden plot twist. In the heart of this country, we found exactly what we needed to ensure a successful future. My parents raised their children with certain morals and values. These morals and values were instilled in them as children and then passed on to us. As hallowed as they are, these morals and values are not purely Colombian. Once in the United States, it was the people along the way and over the years that taught me what it means to be a citizen of the United States. I learned the incredible history and encouraging culture of my new home and even more significantly, I experienced it through the friendships that I made. The open arms that welcomed us, the open minds that accepted us, and the open hearts that appreciated us were the lessons that revealed our nightmare was actually a dream. There were several angels that appeared in our lives just when and where we needed them. Without these individuals (whose names I would rather not share), our success here most certainly would have led to our deaths in some way or another. Furthermore, I have been fortunate in my travels. Almost every state, of over forty that I have visited, has had within it a valuable memory. This is a country that is impossibly alluring with a complex, inspiring, and tragic history.

September 11, 2001

I wanted to share some of the most vivid memories I have of our early years being here. I came from a country where things like the attack on the World Trade Center were not uncommon, and sometimes more deadly. This, however, did not mean that they were any less jarring. It is interesting what a child remembers. In particular, there were two memories glued to me since that Tuesday morning in September.

I.

The first memory that attached to me was of violence, terror, and death. We were all getting ready for our day as was the usual routine in the morning. My dad turned on the morning Spanish news, as he normally did, with the volume up so he could hear it while he shaved in the bathroom. I was working on breakfast; we were behind schedule. We tended to take advantage of the fact that we lived so close to school. With about ten minutes left until the top of the eight o'clock hour, the breaking news music came on. The tone on the voice of the morning news anchor was extremely somber. Not once did I ever pay attention to the news. It was just background noise to me, but there was a cadence I was accustomed to and today she did not bring it. The feeling lives in my memory as the sound of a piano dropping from a major chord to a minor one. She had all of our attention. Seemingly there had been what appeared to be a terrible accident. An airplane had crashed into the North Tower of the World Trade Center. Whatever the hell that place was, I did not know; but the image on the screen started to poke at a sleeping bear as it hibernated in the cave of our memories. We were most certainly late for school that day. Everyone was.

"That is so terrible," my mom spoke with her everlasting empathy. "Those people must be so scared." Besides that, none of us uttered a word. We watched in awe as we heard about possible unconfirmed reports that the airplane might have been hijacked. Other unconfirmed reports said that it was all a communication accident from the control towers. I must mention that even though we had only been in the country for a year, I already understood the world power that is the United States. It was not difficult to identify it as such, as I was aware of where we came from. Therefore I knew that the majority of the world was witness to what happened next. From the angle of the images we had on our screen, a second airplane appeared. In an eternal instant, the airplane kept lowering until it made impact with the second tower. All at once, every human who watched that broadcast knew the United States was under attack. Inside our souls, the feeling window of safety was cracked and the bear that had once quietly nestled was awoken. I wondered if the entire world was this kind of place. We ended up being over an hour late for school. Others stayed home for the day. The teacher spoke her thoughts on the situation while we watched on the television in the classroom. Then, the South Tower collapsed. By now, my English was more than enough to understand the news. We watched as more violence ensued. News reports came one after the other, confirming the planes that had been hijacked. There were more. When the North Tower collapsed, we had already learned that all flights had been grounded and that an attack was the only explanation. This was perhaps the only time in our lives in the United States that we felt genuinely unsafe. The entire country did.

II.

The second vivid memory that attached to me from the day of the attacks was of what happened after the country held its breath in the hours following the collapse of the North Tower, effectively marking the end of the attack and the beginning of the ensuing difficult questions and unidentifiable answers. It was during these hours—and beyond—that I witnessed the country shake off the ashes and stand in united solidarity signaling the world that it would not be moved. This country held to its identity through the concepts of unity, compassion, and empathy. This was as much of a foreign identity to me as I was to it. What I witnessed was people coming together to mourn and hold space for such a traumatic and historic event. This is something at the time that neither my parents or myself had witnessed. As the news continued to shed light on all the mystery surrounding the attack, there immediately began to be a rally to contact and help any people who were directly or indirectly affected by the events of that day. Financial support and Good Samaritan volunteers poured out from all over the country. An appreciation for this special characteristic of the culture of the United States is not only worth mentioning, it is overdue as a reminder to all of us. A reminder that in times of struggle and pain, the best solution is always unity, compassion, and love. This was what made us realize that being citizens of this nation would not only be necessary for our survival, but it would also be an honor and a privilege to do so. As foreigners, the journey would still be long and arduous. We had moved from our home out of the need for survival. We arrived with that mentality. Now we knew that in order to be part of this community, in order to be able to call this place home, we had to learn and adopt these cultural differences to the best of our ability. From survival we began to gravitate towards assimilation. We had to walk the tightrope of identity and culture across two countries or risk becoming foreigners to both.

12

JULIAN

August 2000

I.

While I was learning English and attempting to assimilate myself into school, my dad was starting a new job. After he had his time cleaning horse shit my dad decided to find a job that paid more. Meat packing plants was the next option. His degree was worth nothing without a work permit. So he took whatever he could find. At five-thirty every morning, he would wake up to take the carpool van that he and his coworkers traded driving. Splitting gas allowed them to squeeze every penny out of the cents the job seemed to pay relative to the work. Dressed for the conditions of the freezer he operated in, his job was to skin the cattle that came through the line and eventually ended up in some dinner table of a family much more fortunate. During one of the trips, one of his coworkers asked what he did for a living in Colombia. He made the mistake of telling the truth instead of just lying and saying he was a peasant worker. He never knew how or why someone told his supervisor that he had a college degree and a successful business, or if that was the only part of the story the supervisor clung onto with anger, but what is certain is that he turned my dad's work life into a living hell. Yelling obscene words at my dad and constantly reminding him that he himself was an uneducated man born in the United States, the son of an immigrant who came from Central America and that now he was the superior of a businessman with a college degree. That if my dad as much as protested he would have Immigration Services come and deport him, never to see his family again.

From there, he would come home after a twelve-hour shift at seven-thirty, eat, and shower. Always running late for his job working for a man who owned a cleaning business. My dad's job was to go around the floors of different grocery stores in town. This he would do until one in the morning. Repeat it again, five or six days per week. This continued for a year. To this day, I do not recall a single instance—not a single one ever—in which I heard my dad complain.

II.

After dropping us off to school in the morning, my mom headed back to the house and took the van to work. Her job was different. She reported to the soybean company mainly employing immigrants in town. Her job was to stand in the assembly line and pick out any soybean or onion that looked rotten. With minimum wage and even less breaks. She did that through six-thirty in the evening, coming home to start dinner for dad. My job after school got out at four was to walk home with Danny, come through the backdoor, and make us ramen in the microwave. After her ten-hour shift, she would sit at home and began to sift through the documents she had been able to gather before our departure from Colombia. She would keep anything of value. Since we had no access to the internet, she started getting books in the library about immigration law and, in her broken English, began trying to understand what the process was in order for us to gain any sort of legal working status. In her limited English she realized what the next steps were. There was a Hail Mary shot that we could gain legal status in the United States if we went the route of what was called the right of political asylum. Basically, we had to prove to a court that if we went back to Colombia we would get murdered because of our situation with the FARC. So as my parents learned about this, they realized that the next move was to find a good immigration lawyer. So they did just that. This continued for my mom until we got out for the summer. She had taken her vacation during winter break, the week we learned to make a snowman. Now she needed something where she could take us to work. That summer, Danny and I spent every day of the summer going with mom to work as one of the housekeepers at a hotel. She couldn't afford a sitter. I got particularly good at making beds quickly with Danny. That was our job in each room. As the summer went on, we crossed the one-year mark of having arrived. School was almost here again and things had changed. As was the case with my dad, my mom never complained.

September 2000

Before the hotel rooms, and the snowman and the winter, my mom and dad had saved enough money to get us an appointment with an immigration lawyer. Beginning on the Saturday after Danny's birthday, we drove every single Saturday for the next four years to meet with an immigration lawyer named Lisa Castro. Lisa was born in the United States but her parents came from Venezuela. They did not obligate her to speak Spanish (only around the house) so hers was the first I ever heard to have the accent of a person with English as their first language. A strange sound it was for I had never met someone who spoke Spanish as their second language. She was a well-dressed woman; however, her clothes were not new. Already after only two months of wearing clothes from garage sales, I had developed the ability to spot secondhand clothes in an instant. Of all the things I remember from this period of my life, the drive to Omaha is one of the memories I have most detailed in my brain from the sheer number of times we went to see her. First hurdle was submitting all the right paperwork with all the right evidence. Even what my mom had brought was not enough. For months, people sent us more and more documents, photographs, video recordings, or anything else that might have proved useful.

The risk we ran, as it was explained to us by my parents, was that once we admitted to being here past the six months that our visas allowed us to, we expose ourselves to be deported. If political asylum was denied, we would have to try our luck in Canada. The first opportunity to achieve it was to have a judge decide if our case warranted asylum or not. If he decided not, we were not immediately rejected but our case would then move to a judge who would hear our testimony. Before all of that however, we needed to put the case together as best as possible. So no matter the weather, we went to Omaha to meet with Lisa and her team in our shitty van, unaware of the actual length of the journey we had just embarked on.

May 2001

Through the grapevine from a person we came to trust over the months we were here, we had heard about a man who owned a lot of properties in Grand Island and was willing to rent them out for a price similar to what we were paying at our glorified cardboard box. My parents took us along to find this man and see if there were any properties we could find that made sense for us to move to, and more importantly to see what kind of papers he required. By this point, my English was good enough to serve as an interpreter of sorts. When we met the man he gave us a fantastic handshake and an enormous smile. He wore a bright-red blazer over his silk navy-blue dress shirt. His white, silk pants hung above his ankles and revealed he wore his summer leather shoes, barefoot. He stepped out of his Porsche and introduced himself as Barty Dish. Despite his eccentric looks, the man was one of the many selfless people without whom we might not have survived. By this point, I knew the entire situation and predicament. My parents never lied. Barty learned that we were working on being able to obtain legal status and we would hear our fate relatively soon. We explained there was a chance we would have to leave. The recommendation from our friend came through because when my parents had me ask Barty about the papers needed to rent from him, he smiled and said, "As far as I am concerned until we hear back about your case, the only papers I care about have presidents on them. If you can pay your rent, you can live in any of my properties. No funny business, keep it clean, and I will give you a month-long lease every month if you need to leave early. On the other hand, if you hear back the news you are looking for, whenever that is, we can take the payments you have made so far and count them as a down payment if you would like to own the house." I had to ask twice about the last part because I did not know that this was even something that could be done. After I interpreted, my parents thought that I had made a mistake. They asked him to clarify with their broken English, and he went on to explain again. Upon understanding, my parents lunged at the man for a hug. Some luck at last.

July 2001

Just before the school year started up again, we got word from Lisa that we had to appear in front of a judge to hear the verdict of our application. Back to Omaha we went on Interstate 80 praying the van would make the trip, wondering everytime if this was the last trip it would make. It made it just fine this time, and we went in front of the judge. There was bad news and good news. Bad news: Our case was not rejected but asylum was not granted so we would have to testify in front of a judge. Good news: We would be granted work permits in order for us to be able to work legally in the country. This permit was only granted during the duration of our case going through the system, and provided that we maintained a clean criminal record. We could finally drive around not worrying if a mere traffic stop would result in our deportation and likely our death. More importantly, this meant that we could purchase the home from Barty. We won this battle in the war for our survival. We remained respectful of the unknown battles up ahead, but at least for us there was no longer any piss—just safety.

Furthermore, my parents could validate their degrees when it came to employment. First, by getting them mailed here, second by going to one of the Universities in Nebraska and having them validate and recognize them as legitimate degrees. I would take this statement to comment on the role "luck" had to play. To me it was God, but if fortune is to blame then I would nominate my parent's story to be placed as an example of the phrase "Fortune favors the brave."

August 2001

The gears had changed. Now my parents could apply for less labor-intensive jobs; however, other barriers began to emerge. Both of my parents were used to Spanish, as the majority of their coworkers spoke it as well. My dad got a job at a university as a driver's education instructor, specifically in Spanish, certified by the state. While working with students was in his talent pool, communication with his coworkers was a new kind of challenge. In true fashion, my dad rose to the occasion and made leaps and bounds toward his mastery of the English language. However, it was still difficult. So, I continued to be the interpreter. Eventually, he ended up working for a nonprofit that helped local farmers know their rights and legal protections if needed for whatever reason.

Most people would say that my dad's legacy will live as a giving, hardworking, and kind nature. He dedicated himself to his children so much that he started a nonprofit himself in order to help underprivileged children (mostly immigrants) have access to sports in the community. Mainly fútbol. What started with eleven quintessential rejects became a sponsored organization providing a sporting outlet for over one hundred children in the community in any given month. Several hundred graduated from high school and twenty-six of them as of the writing of this book are pursuing a secondary education on a fútbol scholarship. I tip my hat to you, Coach. Eventually, he started his own business and continues to grow it, every day. He earned several awards for his outstanding leadership in the state of Nebraska, and once by the first lady of the United States.

My mom on the other hand got a night shift job at the Veteran's Retirement Home. There she had to take care of our elderly veterans. She still claims that this was one of the most impactful jobs she had and that it made her truly appreciate not only this country, but also its veterans. After three years of working night shifts, she was never short on interesting stories involving audacious old men, stories about ghosts that wandered the home, and the grief of watching people pass on.

She was also ready to move on. So she landed at a local non-profit, dedicated to helping families in need. I place this story here because it was a memory of growing up here that I really remember feeling rage at the situation we were in. Some of the other women at work started to occasionally make fun at the way my mom pronounced her words. As the days and weeks went on, the comments became not only more frequent, but more cruel. One day after several months of this experience, they went too far. I have stated before that my mom never complained, ever, about any part of any circumstance we ever found ourselves in since day one of our arrival. This remains true, but on this day something happened that I had never seen in my life until that point, and have only really seen it two other times since. That day, I saw my mom cry for the third time in my life. I was filled with rage. My dad left work and took us with him to pick her up. She was in so much emotional pain that she felt she could not drive.

She ended her work with that nonprofit that day, a Tuesday. By the next Monday, she had accepted an offer to work with the local university through the main campus. Her job was community outreach, and so she helped bridge the gap between the immigrant and Hispanic communities and the rest. Working in partnership with several organizations throughout the state, she went on to be recognized several times by several people (including the governor). Today, I am proud to say that she was directly involved in helping several dozens of local businesses establish themselves. She also earned her master's degree.

During the twenty years my parents have been in the United States, they also housed several hundred people who arrived in the country over the years. Some stayed for a few days, some for a few months. Most of them were Colombian. When they were ready to move on, they did. For a few years, our house became known as the "Colombian Embassy," a home away from home, for others. Of the many lessons my parents gave their children, their passion for helping others spoke the loudest. They gave people what little they had to offer with compassion and faith. They taught us the value of generosity in a world that had been so greedy against us. I fail often in the quest to follow their example, but theirs has been the standard since day one.

January 2003

The years maintained a growth trajectory and jumped to a higher record when the news came that I was going to have a second brother. For the first time in the history of our close family, there would be a United States citizen.

October 2003

There is little doubt that the single blessing we received in our lives since entering the United States was the birth of my second brother, Julian. First and foremost, we were gifted with such a wonderful spirit. I am eleven years his senior and it has been yet another gigantic privilege to be able to have watched him grow into such a spectacular human. To me, he serves as the finest example of deep nobility and loyalty. He grew up, it would seem, without a capacity for selfishness or greed. In quite the opposite fashion, his compassion for others was passed down from his mother and his fantastic sense of humor from his father. Additionally, Julian had a fervor for patience. It became his greatest strength as life tested his endurance. His perspective always shifted towards the scope of simplicity and humility. He developed two major interests over his adolescent years: writing music on his guitar, and World War II. The latter he began on his own just tearing through videos on the internet. The guitar was an entirely different beast altogether. He, the guitar and the music he spoke through it were friends. Lifelong and life-giving. Inside his soul lived a wiser, older one. Only breaking free through the vicariousness of Julian's youth. This soul streamed from any guitar he played on or any lyric he wrote. In this manner, the three connected and produced as beautiful music as life itself. Just as graceful and as tragic. One particular moment of brotherly pride presented itself as an opportunity. We found ourselves in a public garden. Some people were walking around, enjoying a decent day. Our reason for being there was because Julian was scheduled to take his senior portraits that day, so he had his guitar with him as this was such a massive piece of his life. A talented photographer was able to capture what happened next—forever. A young man dressed in a faded charcoal gray suit, a silver tie, and a sharp purple shirt approached me. I was holding the guitar while Julian took pictures without it. The young man asked me if I played and I told him that the real talent was Julian. Once he came over, the young man asked Julian if he knew the song "Something" by The Beatles. Without hesitation, Julian affirmed; he knew all of the songs by The Beatles. The young man was getting married that day and was working with a humble budget: a non-existent one. He was in love and she was on her way. They had found someone to marry them. He lived in Florida and she lived in Washington. (This shit happened for real.) The young man and his now fiancé had met online playing video games. Here they were asking a seventeen-year-old to play at their wedding. It was to be Julian's first gig. The way he handled the situation was something out of a movie. This was raw talent as a performer being put on display. His wisdom in understanding the cadence as he riffed quietly in the background, and then picking up some sound during the spaces in this short amount of time. He performed it acoustically and it was brilliant. A moment that will live with me on the top shelf of memories.

The second reason that Julian's life was such blessing was due to the timing. Without getting ahead of myself, I will leave it at that.

April 2004

The time had come for us to face the reality of the consequences we were confronted with the day of our second appointment. This time we had to testify. The entire family needed to be present. Our lives once again were at the hands of a judge and the ability of Lisa Castro to pull through. With the exception of national holidays, we had driven the four-hour round trip to Omaha every single Saturday since the fall of 2001. The dollars in total expenses to even have made it here were enough for a down payment on a house eight times the size of the one we had upgraded to and were currently paying a mortgage on. Add this dollar amount to the tab already filled with intangibles of impossible sacrifices. The things they made us give, after having taken most of the rest. For what could not have been anything less than more than the thousandth time, I watched and listened as my dad gave his testimony in English. The story that I had heard being retold and with more specific details to provide a solid argument that our lives were worth saving. From the start of the sand business to the encounters with the FARC. The explosion at Copey and then the fact that we were being followed. We shared about our love for this country while having to face the pain and admit that the one we came from was not good enough, on record. Finally, he explained how if we went back, our lives would more than likely be in real peril and that we understood the risk of coming forth and seeking permission to stay. As in, we knew this was the last branch we were hanging onto to avoid imminent death.

Once my dad finished his testimony, the judge asked my mother some questions about the story my dad had just told. She nailed her part as did we with the questions we were asked. He even asked if we had gone to Disney yet. Once we all sat down, the room went silent, for a while. The judge shuffled around his papers, underlined and circled some pages and kept sifting through. He followed standard operation procedure. When the silence broke, he addressed us, smiled, and let us know that we were now officially safe from the FARC in the United States under the right of political asylum. The tightrope balancing act of two countries and cultures had now reached a new crisis level in our national identity.

December 2006

I.

It is interesting what a teenager remembers. There were fifteen minutes left of the school day when our principal came on the intercom with a grim tone, "Will the following students please report to the auditorium immediately:..."

I waited as the list went on without rhyme or reason. It did not seem to be in alphabetical order or by grade. Eventually, there was only one common theme that appeared as the names were being called. A familiar fear began to sink my heart as the list continued for several minutes. Not a person in the classroom moved a centimeter. We were all being glued to our desks by the realization that, after several dozen names, this kind of assembly was going to bring with it sinister news. There were eight minutes left of the school day when some of my close friends and classmates grabbed their belongings and headed towards the auditorium. The frosty air of the afternoon in December had found its way into the hallways and classrooms of Walnut Middle School.

There were over one hundred names that were read. All of them Hispanic.

My name was never called. After school, I waited in the foyer for my mom to pick me up, as was the daily routine. This afternoon, I had been waiting for an hour after school was over. Suddenly, all of the students whose names had been called started coming out. No cars were there waiting for them. Most of them had tears streaming down their face.

"What's going on?" I asked one of my friends, as she came to me looking for an embrace.

"Our parents got deported, today and—" she struggled to finish.

"Wait, what?" I asked. "How? Wait, wait, wait. What?"

"ICE came and raided the packing plant. They rounded up our parents and they are being deported. They are gone."

I was gutted. Most of these students had just received news that both of their parents had been relocated. That afternoon, I watched over one hundred classmates and close friends walk empty to their vacant homes in December, their parents would not be there to pick them up, or to make it all okay.

Thirty minutes later, my mom arrived to pick me up. She had been crying. I hugged her tight because I knew that some of her friends were gone. She began to sob. I hugged her tight because I knew as well as she did that it could have been us. It was only the fifth time I had seen my mom cry in my life. I hugged her tight because all that separated us from the human beings who were deported that day was luck.

II.

The packing plant was the largest employer in Grand Island. In total, over 1,300 hardworking, engaged immigrant parents had been put on a bus and then tossed over the southern border. The town was devastated. However, what happened that evening and the days and weeks that followed really gave us hope. There were loud voices throughout the town loudly proclaiming that it was the right decision for the government to have done this. The majority of the town, though, seemed to come together to focus on the real issue: the children. Support from all corners of the state and country poured in as the raid had made national news. The community came together and gave the kids food, shelter, and support where it was needed. The ones who could stay with relatives did so, and for the ones who did not have that privilege, there were teachers, police officers, and other private members of the community who took in the kids until everything was sorted out. Not enough praise can be given to the way in which our community united to put humanity first. This was the first wake-up call I had witnessed of the reality of the lives of an immigrant. In my heart, I began to understand what the next challenge of our lives would be. Fear manifested itself against us as persecution, solitude, poverty, and even death. But now, fear began to wear a new mask to meet me. The mask of discrimination and racism.

March 2007

The years that followed became the transition period that changed our perspective, our identity, and our focus. We were no longer in danger from death. What remained now was the realization of what it means to be a person of color in the United States. Despite what some outlets say or some famous people believe, from firsthand experience, I can say that racism faced us to different degrees and in distinct situations. The reality of deep-seated beliefs in fear and hatred towards something different. This applied to many demographics simultaneously. While strides have been made in history towards the inclusion of Hispanics, problems remain even today, perhaps in a worse way now than can be remembered in recent memory. It is interesting what a child remembers. Perhaps it was there all along and I was too naive to see. In any case, we began to learn that within the immigrant population with Hispanic ethnicity exists another crisis of identity. Hispanic people can be white, black, brown, and any other color or race. Some Hispanics consider Hispanic as a race. The white ones identify as both, and Black Hispanics identify as Black. (If you are confused, welcome to the club.) Among countries, there exists animosity. We are the most racist people toward Hispanics.

We navigated these discoveries because now we were able to focus on the world we would live in. We purchased an even bigger home because Julian now needed his own room. So in 2005, we purchased a home in the neighborhood where once upon a time, an old man was angry that I delivered his paper, just like my dad had said we would end up doing. My parents never lied. However, seven years in and still no Mickey.

Our first winter in that house we put up Christmas lights in our home. This was the first time we ever did this. Out front, the most fucking perfect snowman built by a group of humans. It was here that my parents began to emerge as leaders in the community in the first place. The tightrope loosened and our balance struggled. We kept hanging on to what started to fade from memory to fiction. Colombia started to become foreign. However, one thing that allowed me to have a grasp on the past was the iPod my parents had bought me. Being able to purchase music on the internet allowed me to hear music I had not heard in years. Michael Jackson and Diomedes Diaz blasted through our home at full volume and for the first time since our arrival, we felt at home.

This was most likely due to the fact that what we transitioned our focus to what was now becoming naturalized citizens. "Everybody wants a blue one," my mom had said in Miami the day we arrived. My parents never lied. Our primary focus was survival. At all costs. We had not thought much further past obtaining asylum. After our experience with the system in place as of now, we learned that it had several issues in need of serious innovation and change.

What I have come to realize is that the system is backwards. The next steps were now to wait and avoid prison. Even that would not have disqualified us entirely. The prime hurdle of the process was reaching asylum. It should be the other way around. After having had our status for a year and some months, we were able to apply to become residents of the United States. The well-recognized Green Card. We were just one step away. Nothing guaranteed until it was given, but if everything went according to plan, we were four to five years away.

March 2012

For some reason or another (I can't remember. Interesting, right?), my parents were given their dates for citizenship before me. Everything went according to plan. They had made it. The five-year wait brought its own victories. My mother obtained her master's. My father started his business. I graduated from high school and was about to meet Rachel. Danny was excelling in sports. Julian was doing "fine and dandy," as he would say. The pains of these years were significant, too. We hurt for home. Colombia's beauty in our memories had faded. Twelve years tend to do that. The recession left my dad without a job and financially, things didn't go as planned. Might have been the thousands of dollars we spent to get asylum, pay for the lawyers, applications, and gas. Might have been that customs take more than eight years to learn and there exists minimal financial guidance for the middle class in general, let alone such guidance in Spanish. Especially not at those times when richer people feasted on the desire for people, especially immigrants, to purchase a home and then caused the world economy to collapse and turn around and blame immigrants for stealing jobs. But, as I stated before, not once did my parents complain.

Instead, the years fighting to succeed and get ahead drove my parents apart. So, shortly after they received their citizenship, they divorced. I heard Chris Rock once do a bit about marriage and how difficult it can be. He talks about Nelson Mandela spending twenty-seven years in a miserable prison. Starving, being tortured, and barely hanging on. Then, Nelson was free and within six months, he was divorced. "That's how hard marriage is! Nelson came out of prison and said, 'I can't take this shit anymore!'" This is the perspective I leaned towards while it all happened. Perhaps Danny has a few, but I was most likely the only one who remembers a time where my parents were affectionate toward each other. It is interesting what a child remembers.

Life, in its own way, has a way of driving a wedge, and in human history, few have claimed to have lived perfectly. However, as it started to crumble, that perspective became harder to find. I am glad to say that both of my parents are currently remarried happily. More importantly, especially for Julian, they are very cordial. We are able to be in the same space without awkward moments and their respective spouses get along well with their opposite and with their mirror. Even so, the ripples of the divorce can be felt to this day. Past memories watching over that hibernating bear revisit to remind us they are there sometimes. Some of these are not ready to be put into words just yet.

13

THE SECRET

Without question Julian's birth was the clearest and most important Godsent event in our lives as a family. The timing alone was critical. His place in our timeline will forever be the divine intervention of bliss, grace, and happiness that we needed to have survived the emotional toll we suffered at the news of the first death since our departure of someone in the family who we had left behind.

July 2000

Before the behemoth that became the internet, international communication was significantly more difficult. Shortly after our arrival, I learned about international calling cards. If you are unaware, these cards are still used today. They work by having a certain value in dollar amount, and providing the user with a set amount of corresponding minutes. Each card was the size of a credit card, equal in shape, cut, and weight. They each had printed on them a six- to ten-digit number uniquely assigned to that card. Once we dialed the number, the automated machine in its robotic tone let us know the number of minutes of communication left on the card. It would then ask for the international number for the country we were trying to reach, followed by the phone number we would like to dial. The constant issues we had with these cards was the inconsistency of the amount of minutes the card started off with, and that it was inconsistently keeping time. We had ten-minute conversations that burned through thirty-five minutes of card balance.

Four days after we had left, our family back home got word that we had made it safely to safety. This was the first of several thousands of cards we consumed before Facebook and Skype allowed us to use video communication for relatively cheap. Several thousands of dollars to add to the tally of the cost of being an immigrant.

April 2003

A year before Julian was born, my tío Joaquín on my dad's side had an opportunity to bring his family to live in Nebraska, and after debating it for a long time, he took it in April. They would stay with us until they got on their feet. While the house became somewhat cramped for the first few months, we were happy to have some familiarity of home with us. Their arrival helped put my parents at ease. However, on the second call home, the news came. Cancer had been discovered in Grandma Adela's digestive system. The outlook was not positive. By now, I was ten years old and well aware of the impossible situation my dad and his brother were in. The likelihood of them seeing their mother in person again was practically zero. The news stunned me with a grief deeper than any I had experienced in my short ten years of living, and since. I never became accustomed to that feeling, no matter how many times I experienced it. Time stands still and the simple act of breathing drags your full concentration. Remaining standing still became a challenge. My brain struggled to buffer the memory of her. I searched and scratched the deepest parts of my mind palace, searching for any and all memories of the woman who had been the most influential in the past, the present, and the future of my life. Often, I recall the last day I saw her. When she hugged me last and told me we would see each other again.

October 2003

I.

As the months rolled by, we all felt the paradox of life and death as we simultaneously processed the excitement of my mom's pregnancy with Julian and the saddening news of Adela's deterioration. As we burned through expensive calling cards with the little money we could afford to use, the news became worse and worse. Typically, we would purchase a month's worth of cards in one visit to any local Hispanic store. As the condition developed and the cancer spread, we began to purchase that same amount every week. Luckily, we could split it between the two families that now spent several evenings per week crouched down around the phone listening to updates and sharing our own. My cousins had started school, Julian was growing strong and steady.

Eventually, we began to buy the month's worth of cards every day. Adela was losing. Of course, not for a lack of trying. That crazy old woman was fighting with every bit of her might to not only give hope to those back home, but to all of us in the United States. The cancer would have to take her alive. On our end, the question became: Is this going to be the last time we talk? The thought terrorized us in two ways.

For one, knowing it could be, the conversations became longer with each one of us, nine in total. The uncertainty made us have to say goodbye as if it was the last time everyday. It was the kind of terror that is tragically beautiful, and chilling.

Second, we all understood that one day for certain, it would be the last time. As in, we would eventually be right, with the possibility of such a day increasing daily. The guilt started to seep more and more every day. We would not go to the funeral. This was the price we paid.

On October 8, 2003 it happened. After months of waiting, Julian was born. Timing is everything. The bliss of meeting the first person in our family to be born in the United States. What a special place in the generational timeline. Julian brought with him that day, and every day since, a light in our lives that reminded us of the beauty of life with him in it. Without him in our lives, it is impossible to say which dark corner of life we would have found ourselves in by then. On October 16, 2003, I woke up in my parents' bed to the sound of the phone going off. It was early in the morning as the sunrise was in its infancy.

"Hello?" said my dad. "What time?"

And then I don't remember what happened after that.

II.

I believe my dad would have gone into a severe depression had Julian not been born just eight days before he hung up the phone that morning. Still the bliss and blessing of a newborn son, especially given the circumstances, was barely enough to keep my dad's grief at a relatively healthy level—if such a thing exists. The news about it all leveled the entire family. None of us went to school that week. As for my dad, he took two off of work. The guilt that followed was burning in the front of our minds. There would be a funeral. We would not go. We could not go. To this day, the fact that I don't recall the last words she said to me chews at my heart. Thousands went to her funeral. They gathered from all corners of the country and even from other parts of the world. A variety of rich, poor, young, and old gathered to pay their respects to her. Of course they did. After living life in the way that she did, with such joy and with such grace, her legacy brought them there. Adela's love extended to not only the people she met over her festive life, but also to the people who met her family. The way she loved and lived was simple to imitate but impossible to duplicate, so her children and their children learned to do so as best as they could. Thousands went to her funeral.

I didn't go.

I couldn't go. I wanted to go more than I wanted to go to Disney and see Mickey. Life, with its twisted turns, brought danger and so we ran. A one-way ticket in search of refuge that cost more than money could pay. We paid a price for our lives and it cost us the ability to bid farewell to hers. Not a day passed where we missed the reminder of what it all had cost us. We had lost the brightest and kindest person in our family. We needed fucking permission to say goodbye. That evening, we all sat in the living room holding the other as we cried. Later on, we kept on with what was to come next. Her ashes would be placed in a church near the neighborhood where she spent so much of her time walking through the parks and the woods, bringing light into the lives of others. The positive in this was that she was no longer suffering. Wherever she went, she was at peace, and this was also a way for my dad and my tío Joaquín to cope with the loss of their mother.

December 2003

The reality of the situation would take years to set in. Memories were clinging on and they were some that I never really picked, but they kept clinging. But it wasn't until this Christmas that we were reminded of the kind of person Adela was. We spent our days exchanging daily phone calls after the funeral. International calling cards became as important as groceries. They were our only connection to news from home and our only coping mechanism. As my tío Joaquin and the family began to experience their first winter, we had just finished teaching them how to build a snowman. On that day everything changed. On one of our phone calls it was revealed to us that on the day my tío Joaquín had announced that he was leaving with his family to the United States, Adela was planning on giving us the news that she had cancer. She was going to tell everyone that in her checkup, the doctors had spotted a growth in her digestive system and that luckily, the prognosis was favorable but still should be taken seriously. My grandma knew once she had heard her son bravely announce he was going to chase a better life for his children, she didn't have the heart to tell them about her diagnosis. It would have kept them in Colombia and they would have never left afterwards. So she kept her secret. Months went by and the cancer spread, and by the time April of 2003 came around, Adela was past the point of no return. Once she knew they were safe in Nebraska she decided to tell us all.

She sacrificed her life for her son and his family. To ensure that they could have a life of opportunity and peace. Adela knew when her other son left she would never see him again. Hugging her grandchildren for the last time, she smiled as her body was growing the very thing that was killing her. She smiled so that their last image of her would be a happy one. She smiled because she always did, and as I have been told, she smiled right to the very end.

14

THE BLUE ONE

May 2012

During my freshman year of college, I was approached by a fellow student named Steve who spoke to me about a summer internship opportunity. Over the phone, Steve told me all about this program where "the average student made $9,000 for the summer and there was an opportunity to travel and gain college credit." My parents raised me to live by my word and, because I had committed to going to this informational session, I went reluctantly.

It was here that a young woman named Morgan went through her PowerPoint on all of the advantages of the summer program. She informed me that this program was with Southwestern Advantage, a one-hundred-fifty-year-old company based in Nashville that published educational systems made up of books and websites. Students were in charge of selling these products through a system of referrals and recommendations all over the United States. It was a twelve-week-long program where every student faced the challenge of working eighty hours per week while being away from their hometown. Here, Morgan claimed that the sales training and challenge would give me great experience to show on my resume and share during interviews in the future while seeking employment after graduation. They mentioned the all-inclusive vacation awarded to the students who earned anything above the average of $9,000 over the course of the summer. Morgan enthusiastically explained the adventures of the northeast coast of the United States, where students could visit landmarks and participate in activities that the typical college student did not get to enjoy.

I listened and learned. I was intrigued by the idea of this company so I applied for an interview.

Now, following the informational session, I realized not everyone is as open-minded as I believed. It would be a lie to say that I was supported in my decision after mentioning this to my social circle. Skeptics lined up to chime in on how this whole program sounded like a scam. Everyone gave me their own version of the old "sounds too good to be true" mentality. So, I decided to call the only people in the world who I knew would support me: my parents. Even this didn't work out as well as I had planned. My mother was skeptical and my dad was indifferent. But I explained everything I had learned and everything I wanted to gain, and in the end I gained their support. They explained to me that they did their best to raise me in such a way that they hoped by now I had learned to make good decisions.

I did.

I got accepted as one of the 3,000 students who were going to participate that summer. The first week I went through an electric crash course on sales. I was moved by the fascinating speakers and the incredible students who were also selected for the program. From there, off to the summer I went. Hornell, New York, was my assigned territory and the town I would call home for the next few months. First order of business: find a host family. Some of the other students already had housing set up for the summer. My roommates Steve (who I met two weeks prior) and Josh (who I met in Nashville) came up with a game plan: we would visit local churches and simply make an announcement before each service about who we were and what we were looking for. We were college kids from Nebraska working in New York for the summer. All we needed was a place to sleep for the night since we were gone by 6:30 a.m. and home around 10 p.m, Monday through Saturday. On Sundays, we would go be tourists. We bought our own food, made our own meals, and paid rent. In the small town of Hornell, there were nine services we picked to go to.

Early Sunday mornings, we split up with a goal to each go to three different services throughout the morning and early afternoon. Josh, who was Catholic, visited the three Catholic churches. Steve and I split the other six. I had not attended a church in several years, and now here I was attending three different services from three different churches.

Asking the pastors to make the announcement and giving the announcement itself was simple. I was about to sell books door-to-door and, luckily for me, public speaking came naturally. I kept thinking that by playing the game of numbers, at least one of us would surely find someone who would be interested in hosting us.

o for 9.

We met again after the last Catholic service let out. We felt defeated but determined. A quick Google search gave us one last place to go; an afternoon service at the Rehoboth Deliverance Ministry that we were twenty minutes late to. We hurried to the church and as we entered, we immediately felt out of place. None of us had ever attended a predominantly Black church. We sat at the only pew left open—the very front. The energy was electric as we entered in the middle of a worship song and it maintained despite the numerous people who turned to look at three of us as we made our way towards our seats. We sat slightly uncomfy, but mainly fascinated. What an experience!

Then came the sermon.

Without losing the energy of the room, the pastor preached. The text: Isaiah 40:31. "You see when a storm comes, all of the animals seek shelter. The mighty mountain lion, the fearsome grizzly bear, and the strong buffalo! They all hide when they see the storm! But not the eagle. The eagle accepts the storm. It embraces it and flies towards it! Just when the wind gets strongest, it uses it to fly over the storm, and rises above!" The vibe was positively contagious.

After the service, several friendly people approached us to chat. We mingled through the people until someone tapped my shoulder. There she was. Time had given her a charm perfectly displayed by the wrinkles on her white skin. There was a lovely kindness in her eyes that paired splendidly with the joy that looked up at me. She said her name was Rita and that she might be able to help us.

Rita had a house with two bedrooms available and no rent to charge in Canisteo, a five-mile drive south of Hornell. This was one of the many blessings this summer had in store. I spent the entire summer approaching families and talking to them about the industry-leading products that the company offered and was touched by the receptiveness of the people in the western part of the state of New York. I learned about connections, networking, and making effective first impressions. I learned how to run a business and to push my mind and body further than I thought I ever could. My skin turned to steel through the rejection of close-minded people who refused to sit with me for ten minutes to talk about education. I learned the value of treating everybody with respect regardless of their behavior toward me because, simply put, it was not my place to judge a person's character by their actions when I was clueless as to what led to their behavior in the first place. I learned the importance of living by discipline and that hard work beats talent when talent doesn't want to work hard. I saw a part of the country that I had never seen before and visited some of the most astonishing locations on the planet; places like the Empire State Building, New York City and Niagara Falls. I went skydiving! Most importantly, I met some lifelong friends that forever impacted my life for the better. These were the people who encouraged me and believed in me even when I did not believe in myself. These were the people who reminded me that life is ten percent what happens to you and ninety percent what you do about it. These were the people who showed me attitude isn't everything, it is the only thing.

Then I came home.

Oh and about the money. I made $20,000, and although universities would like to claim otherwise, I will never find a place where I can pay twice that amount, and from that same place, gain half the experience that I did during the summer. This unfortunately created a situation I did not expect because my success in the summer also meant I had won the all-inclusive trip to Mexico. Since it had been months since my parents became citizens and still not a single correspondence for my appointment date, I still would need to both get permission from the government to leave the country and have to travel as a Colombian national. The latter was the most infuriating of the two without comparison. Due to the aforementioned, not-so-fabulous history of Colombians, traveling anywhere was a nightmare. To further complicate the matter, my passport had expired.

October 2012

That month I had to take a trip to Chicago. In order to renew the passport so I could travel, I would have to visit the Colombian consulate at 500 Michigan Avenue in Chicago. More fucking lines, signs and buildings. Luckily, from my earnings that summer, I could pay to have the passport expedited as well as the expenses that went into: flying to Chicago and back on the same day, obtaining a passport photo, applying for a Colombian identification document, obtaining the document on the same day, going to a different floor in the building with this identification document, applying for the passport and finally obtain it, then applying for a visa for the Mexican government to allow me to enter the country, and talking to my lawyer about me going to Mexico as a resident to make sure I was not jeopardizing citizenship hope. All of this would most likely cost more than the trip I had won and I was against the clock. For the day I spent in Chicago, I just focused on getting my brown little book and getting home to work on the application. As I watched paint dry in the waiting room, a man walked up to me with a manilla envelope.

"Here you go. Enjoy your travels!" said the man in a friendly tone.

"Thanks again for all your help. This is huge. Do you know of any good Colombian restaurants in Chicago?" I asked.

"Yes. I can write some down for you, and you can take a cab or train there. Lincoln Avenue is the best for that."

"That would be great!" I replied. I took the paper from after he wrote three names. I was determined to make the most out of this visit to the Windy City. Nebraska did not have a single Colombian restaurant, so I was there to eat. After some *sancocho* and some *arepas*, I enjoyed the most delicious *bandeja paisa* that I have enjoyed in North America. With this delightful meal, I left Chicago in high spirits. Upon landing in Omaha, I opened a text from my mom.

"CALL ME," said the text message. Immediately I dialed.

"Hello, my oldest baby!" said my mom on the other end. I will always be a baby in her eyes.

"Hello, mama," I replied. "Is everything okay?"

"Yes! I wanted to let you know that a package from the Department of Homeland Security arrived for you today. You have a Test and Ceremony date. It is for two weeks from now. Andrés, you are going to be a citizen of the United States."

I looked down at the brown little book in my hands as we stayed on the phone in silence. Even if somehow we could say a word, none were needed, our tears said it all.

November 2012

It is interesting what a twenty-year-old remembers. Lines, signs, buildings. The Department of Homeland Security just outside of Omaha. Of course, I wore a suit. It's worth looking the best you can for the best days of your life. I arrived ninety minutes early for my appointment because there was bound to be a line. Especially for these kinds of things, meaning that they do not occur often enough. However, the wait for this line was worth more than even Disney, I imagined. I guess my dad was right: A visa is like a ticket to Disney. My parents never lied. Here we were twelve years later and we hadn't even been to Florida since we first arrived. This thought led me down memory lane as I waited in line under the sign that said "Citizenship Test" in English. I remembered everything.

June 2005

I remembered the day I saw my dad again after the bus ride from Miami to Memphis on July 14, 2000. Danny and I kept rubbing his beard; we couldn't believe it was him. I remembered being eight and trying to build a snowman. I remembered being eleven when Julian was born on October 8, 2003. The first United States citizen in the family. I remembered how eight days later Grandma Adela lost the fight to cancer: October 16, 2003. She never meant to lie.

Just as importantly, I remembered the day I met Rolando. To this day Rolando remains one of my best friends. Most people just called him Lando. (You're welcome. You know who you are.) Somewhere I heard the description of this kind of friend that you make in life. Lando was the kind of best friend that if I were in jail, I would not be able call him to bail me out. He wasn't broke, he would just be in the jail cell with me. His family was Guatemalan. He was the only child of a single mom. Naturally, they were close given the kind of love she gave him. One of the most fantastic mothers I have ever met (and after all those summers selling books door-to-door, I have met a lot of moms). Lando had his wild moments. So over the years we built a variety of memories that included multiple legitimate near-death experiences, audacious secrets, and outrageous circumstances. He was also successful in keeping me from making the most blatantly ridiculous and dangerous decisions. Lando will forever remain in my life and it is among the highest honors in my life that I was in his wedding and present at the birth of his first child. However, Lando's grandpa was a key figure in our story. This man owned a business that hired my dad to teach and prepare people for the citizenship test. My dad had developed a class that guaranteed the student to pass the citizenship test or the class was free until they did.

During the summer that year and over breaks that fall, I helped my dad in the class because, luckily for me, I had learned to pronounce the words like the person giving the test would. Therefore, the students could prepare for the spoken portion of the test. So, I remembered everything. I remembered being seven and the smell of urine in the house we first arrived at in Nebraska. I remembered being thirteen and putting up our first ever Christmas lights at the house we moved into as owners and I remembered being the child interpreter for my parents everywhere we went. I remembered being seventeen when my dad gave a speech in English as he received his award for leadership excellence in the state of Nebraska. I remembered being eight and going to work with my mom and helping her make the beds of the hotel rooms so we could go home sooner. I remember being sixteen when she earned her master's degree from a United States university. I remembered being eighteen and getting kicked out of a public park by the police for playing soccer on a basketball court. I remembered being nineteen and my friends coming over for the New Year's celebration and embracing my culture by learning to dance salsa. I remembered the worried look on my parents faces during the countless drives to Omaha to meet with the expensive immigration lawyers. I am happy to say I passed the test.

November 2012

I.

The woman who proctored the interview and test stepped out of the room after a lackluster congratulations for what had been the most important moment of my life so far. The ceremony for citizenship is unlike anything else I have experienced as of the writing of this. Everything was surprisingly mundane and straightforward. There were several of us becoming citizens that day. All stories similar and even more dramatic and complex than the one I was living. As I waited for the ceremony to start, my parents arrived with a welcome celebratory meal. I had not eaten since before my test and the feeling of knowing that it was all coming to this moment had starved me. "Congratulations!" said my mom as she hugged me tighter than I could ever remember her doing so.

"I am so proud of you," said my dad trying to hold back tears. I was happy that they were cordial after the divorce. We were still a family. Now it was time to let go of my life as I knew it.

"How does it feel?" I asked my parents. "I am nervous for some reason."

I was working well on my meal. They both just sat there, thinking. I always appreciated when either of my parents took a while to answer an important question as it meant that they were answering from the heart, one of many traits that I strive to learn from them.

"You will never forget it. I promise." My parents never lied. The door to the room where the ceremony was to take place swung open. The same woman who interviewed me waved us in. I hugged my parents who would be able to join me in the room but would have to sit separately. After two deep breaths, I stepped inside. The room was nothing special. Just eight chairs facing a projector screen. Several flags with stars that I was about pledge my allegiance to that I had seen all those years ago at the "home away from home." Where was home? Dual citizenship allowed me to keep my Colombian identity but as much as it pained my heart to do so, part of that identity had to make space for this new accomplishment to move into. I had spent years making sure that the aspects of me that tied me to my heritage remained a part of me. Now the time had come to let some of them go. This is the crisis of identity that most naturalized citizens face. This is the price we pay every day. So many years of constant pressure to prove that I loved the United States and that I deserved to live here. The love that immigrants have for this country should seldom be questioned; rather, the anguish they experience as they mourn the life they knew should be acknowledged and empathized. My thoughts were interrupted by the sound of President Obama's voice coming from the video that was now playing on the projector screen. His eloquent words told the story of the United States and the importance of people like me to the birth, development, and future of the nation. He ended the speech with two words that lifted the barely bearable weight that twelve years had placed in my being: Welcome home. The room faded away for a moment in time that silence inhabited after he said those words. I was too busy to care who gave me my certificate. I wanted to take it and run in case she changed her mind, in case something happened that would cease to make this day real. My mother held me in her arms five minutes later as I wept. It was over.

II.

On November 6, 2012, I became a United States citizen. The greatest accomplishment of my life so far. The trip to Mexico was to be during Thanksgiving break and was rapidly approaching. Naturally, this called for another visit to Chicago to get a different passport—a new one. I thought about how different my life was just a month ago when I received my Colombian one. Here I was again getting an expedited passport. I ended up paying in flights what the vacation cost—completely worth it. An appointment was set for me to take care of the paperwork. A lifeless hallway with several doors loomed ahead once more. These hallways often lacked color to celebrate what purpose this office holds. It made little precious books. Two hours later my hands trembled as I received a manilla envelope with my last name on it. Back in the hallway I opened it. Inside was a blue little book. Everybody wants a blue one.

December 2012

It is interesting what a twenty-year-old remembers. Lines, signs, buildings. This time we found ourselves staring up in wonder at the giant castle famously rooted at the center of the Magic Kingdom park in Walt Disney World. It was New Year's Eve. At least what remained of it. We were there not as "tourists" and needed no "visa." It was magical. Fireworks flew like tears in the sky. Mickey's voice counted down.

Ten.

Nine.

Eight.

The five of us looked at each other behind watery eyes.

Seven.

Six.

Five.

Four.

The seconds flew by as fast as the last twelve years of our lives did.

Three.

Two.

One.

There, on the castle, Mickey appeared.

My parents never lied.

15

ASHES

I.

After I received the ring, we left the apartment. Rachel was holding my hand as I walked toward the church where her ashes are kept. The walk to her church from her apartment had been imprinted in my brain along with the words she told me the last time we were together: "I will see you again." I understood then that she had been right all along. Adela never specified a time for when we would see each other again. The place that she rests is nothing extraordinary, yet humbly special.

"She would have wanted it this way," I said to Rachel. Everything had shrunk over the years and as we walked in for a special service in her honor, I was reminded of her humility. The church was modest, welcoming, comforting, and full of a spiritual bliss. It matched her perfectly. We had returned for this. Nervous to see her, I dressed the best I could, trimmed my beard, fixed my hair, and prayed. It was the best I could do. After the service I could hear my own heartbeat. As I inhaled, I focused on the false reality that I had been holding onto since leaving Colombia: the assumption that I would see her alive. The false reality did not want to leave. In this reality, Adela was not gone. I was not ready for her to be gone. It was time.

We walked over to where she rested. Hundreds of names on a wall holding ashes of other stories and memories. Reality hit as I came across the stone, her name cemented onto it with two dates marking the beginning and end of the life of the most marvelous person I have ever known. The pain of waiting more than a decade for this moment surged from deep inside and overwhelmed me. Thousands went to her funeral and I didn't go. My legs struggled and on my knees I released the pain. She was gone.

II.

It never gets easier. It just develops into a different kind of challenge. As I learned and read about the history of not just my people but of Hispanics in general, I am reminded of how invisible I feel sometimes. In the movies, I became used to looking like the bad guy, the criminal, the rapist, the "illegal." I never saw myself as a superhero in any cinematic universe, as a decorated veteran, as a president. My music was frequently excluded from any sort of variety playlist, and my best food was tacos, burritos, and tortillas. I was never on the winning team or on the right side. The only history that was really taught in school or mentioned in the news was the history of my ancestors. After the Mayans, the Aztecs, and the Incas, tribes that were massacred. Yet we are the ones called murderers, rapists even. Fuck that.

We are not illegal.

We are legacies

Made in the USA
Las Vegas, NV
17 December 2021